Enid Blyton

HE WOULDN'T
GO TO SLEEP

and other bedtime stories

*Illustrated by
Paul Crompton*

D1581920

World International Publishing Limited
Manchester

Published in Great Britain by World International
Publishing Limited,
An Egmont Company, Egmont House, PO Box 111,
Great Ducie Street,
Manchester M60 3BL.
Printed in Italy.

British Library Cataloguing in Publication Data
Blyton, Enid 1897–1968
He wouldn't go to sleep and other bedtime stories.
I. Title II. Series
823.912 [J]

ISBN 0–7498–0313–4

Cover illustration by Robin Lawrie

Contents

Enid Blyton

Enid Blyton was born in London in 1897. Her childhood was spent in Beckenham, Kent, and as a child she began to write poems, stories and plays. She trained to be a teacher but she devoted her whole life to being a children's author. Her first book was a collection of poems for children, published in 1922. In 1926 she began to write a weekly magazine for children called *Sunny Stories*, and it was here that many of her most popular stories and characters first appeared. The magazine was immensely popular and in 1953 it became *The Enid Blyton Magazine*.

She wrote more than 600 books for children and many of her most popular series are still published all over the world. Her books have been translated into over 30 languages. Enid Blyton died in 1968.

He wouldn't go to sleep

Leaper the frog was a fine fellow. He was five years old, so he was quite grown up and felt very proud of himself.

"I am the biggest frog in the ditch!" he said to himself. "I have the brightest green coat, and I am sure that no other frog has legs as long as mine. I can leap almost to the top of the hedge!"

He couldn't really – but certainly he could jump very high, for a frog. Once when a rat was after him, Leaper jumped so high that the rat was afraid and ran away!

Leaper was clever at catching flies, too. He flicked out his tongue, which had a sticky tip, and caught hundreds of flies each summer.

Once a sparrow saw him catching fly after fly, and flew down beside him.

"How do you catch flies so easily?" asked the sparrow. "I would like to take a lesson from you. I cannot catch nearly so many as you, and I have four baby sparrows to feed. Teach me how you do it, frog."

"Well, it's quite easy," said Leaper. "Look – I fling my tongue like this – hit the fly – and bring it back into my mouth on the tip of my tongue."

"Yes, but how do you manage to fling your tongue out so far?" asked the sparrow. "Mine will only go out a tiny way."

"Ah, but I have my tongue fastened to the *front* of my mouth, not to the back," said Leaper proudly. "You see, I can put it out much farther then. Look!"

He flung his tongue out again and hit the sparrow on the beak with it.

"Good gracious!" said the sparrow, in surprise. "Don't do that. I'm afraid, Leaper, that I'll never be able to catch as many flies as you, because my tongue is fastened to the back of my mouth, just as the tongues of children are. Well, well – you are very lucky, I think."

Leaper had a lovely summer. It was rather rainy, and he liked that. His ditch was damp and cool. Flies buzzed everywhere, especially the big bluebottles. Leaper only had to sit under a dock-leaf and wait for the flies to perch nearby – then out would go his tongue, and fly after fly would disappear!

Leaper grew fat. He found a great many green caterpillars and ate those too. He found a family of earwigs and had them for his dinner. He discovered where the slugs came out to feast after a shower, and he ate so many that he really couldn't manage even one more.

Oh yes, Leaper had a marvellous time and enjoyed his life very much. He knew the mice that ran along the ditch. He often talked with the slow, wise old toad who lived under a big stone on the bank. He chatted to the sparrows and said 'how-do-you-do' to the hedgehog that sometimes came shuffling by at night.

The summer passed. The autumn came and acorns tumbled down in the wood. Blackberries grew fat and juicy on the hedges, and children came to pick them.

The grass snake came wriggling along the bottom of the ditch, and Leaper got under a stone at once. The snake sometimes made a meal of a fat frog.

"I can see you!" called the snake. "But you needn't worry. I'm off to sleep the weeks away now!"

"Silly fellow!" said Leaper, as he watched the snake wriggling away. "Going off to sleep in a hollow tree whilst there is so much food to eat!"

It was a warm autumn. Flies still buzzed around, and Leaper had plenty to eat. But the nights were cold. The hedgehog came to say goodbye.

"I have a cosy hole in the bank," he

told Leaper. "I have taken dead leaves and moss into it in my mouth, and now I am going to curl up there, warm and snug, and sleep the winter away."

"Silly creature!" thought Leaper. "What is this idea of sleeping the winter away? I did it for four winters – but now that I am full-grown I shall do as I please. I shall spend the winter awake – and eat all the flies there are! There will be no one to share them with, so I shall have more than ever."

The dormouse hurried along the ditch, fat and brown. "Goodbye, Leaper!" he cried. "I am fat and well, and I am going to curl myself up at the bottom of the hedgerow roots and go to sleep, now that the winter is nearly here. Why don't you go to the pond as the other frogs do?"

"Because I am not going to go to sleep this winter," said Leaper grandly. "It is a waste of time. I shall stay awake and eat everything by myself!"

"How foolish you are!" said the

dormouse, and ran down a hole to its hiding-place under the roots. It curled itself up, put its nose into its paws, and slept.

The old toad called to Leaper.

"Leaper! Go to the pond and settle yourself in the mud at the bottom to sleep! It is time."

"I'm not going to," said Leaper. "I'm going to keep awake for a change! Why don't you keep awake too, old toad?"

"I am wise enough to know what is good for me," said the toad, and he blinked sleepily. "Goodnight! I am going to sleep now. Do not wake me until the spring days are here."

"Foolish toad!" said Leaper, and he laughed croakily. "Nobody is brave enough to keep awake. Well – I will be the first frog to keep awake in the winter. How I shall laugh at all the other creatures when they awake thin and sleepy in the spring and see me here, fat and jolly!"

So one by one all the creatures

disappeared. The bats went. The lizards were nowhere to be seen. The newts had gone. Every frog was at the bottom of the pond, sleeping tight. The toads were under damp stones. The dormice had gone, and the snakes no longer glided along the bottom of the ditch.

Only the rabbits came out to play, and the stoats and weasels hunted them. And sometimes the big rat came slinking along the hedgerow to see what he could find. The frog hid then.

At first there were many flies for him and even a caterpillar or two. The flies came to feast on the ivyflowers that blossomed late on the hedge above. Leaper caught a great many. He liked the warm autumn sunshine – but at night the frost came and put a white covering on the grass.

Then suddenly the flies all went! There was a very hard frost one night – and every fly was killed. Even the spiders now hid themselves away in cracks and corners. Not one was left.

Leaper grew thin. For five days he did not catch a single fly, nor did he find any grub or spider. He began to be worried.

"Perhaps after all it is a wise thing to sleep in the winter," he thought. "I wish now that I had gone down to the bottom of the pond with the others. What am I going to do if no more flies come?"

No more flies arrived. They were all dead. A whole week more went by, and now Leaper was so thin that he looked half his size.

"I shall go to the pond and swim down to the mud," he thought at last. "The others will laugh at me, but I can't help it. I shall die of hunger and cold if I stay up here."

So he began to leap away from the ditch towards the pond. He could not leap as high as usual because he was not so fat and strong. But at last he reached the pond.

And then Leaper stared in very great astonishment. Something had happened to the pond! It was no longer water. He could not slip into it and swim. It was hard, like the earth. What could have happened?

Leaper hopped on to the ice – for the pond had frozen, of course! But no matter how he tried, he could not get through the ice to the mud at the bottom of the pond. So he hopped off again and leapt to another pond he knew. But that was the same! It was quite hard and cold.

"This is most extraordinary," said poor Leaper. "Why did nobody tell me that ponds went hard in the winter? I never knew that before. And I didn't know either that flies disappeared in the cold weather. Dear, dear – I thought I was so clever and wise and strong – and now I find that I know hardly anything! The ones I thought so foolish are the wise ones!"

He hopped away from the ponds. He was frightened, hungry, cold and sad. He knew he would soon die – but it was his own fault.

And then Billy, the spaniel, saw him! Billy was surprised. He was old enough to know that no frogs were about in the winter. He gently picked Leaper up in his mouth and trotted home with him.

Billy had been taught not to hurt anything he picked up, so when he put Leaper down at the feet of his little mistress, the frog was not hurt at all.

Nora, Billy's mistress, was most astonished to see the frog. "Mummy, Mummy!" she called. "Come and see what Billy has brought me – a frog, in the middle of winter!"

Mummy was astonished too. She picked up the thin frog and looked at him. "Poor thing," she said, "he is half dead. Put him into your aquarium, Nora – maybe he will sink to the bottom and sleep in the sand there."

So Leaper was put into Nora's aquarium – and he was sensible enough to swim to the bottom and bury himself in the sand there. He slept at once – and there he still sleeps.

Wasn't it a lucky thing for him that Billy the spaniel found him? I don't think he will be quite so proud or quite so foolish next winter, do you?

One moonlight night

The big round moon shone in at the playroom window, and the toys looked up at it in delight.

"It's so nice to have a lamp shining in the sky tonight," said the pink rabbit. "We can see what we are doing! Shall we play hide-and-seek?"

"No. Let's have a ride in the wooden train," said the teddy bear. "Come on."

"But where *is* it?" said the clockwork clown, looking round in surprise. "It's not here!"

"Good gracious! Where's it gone?" said the little golden-haired doll.

"*I* know!" cried the clockwork mouse. "Don't you remember – the two children took it out to let it run down the garden path, carrying the two little kittens? They must have left it out in the garden."

"Let's go and get it," said the clockwork clown, who enjoyed a bit of an adventure. "Come on – we can all climb out of the window!"

So out they climbed, and slid down the creeper growing up the wall. They set off to the garden path where they had last seen the wooden train. Yes – there it was, with its long line of little wooden carriages.

Well, the toys played round the train for a little while, and then suddenly they stopped.

They all listened – and sure enough it was a little voice from down the garden, shouting loudly.

"Help! Oh, please help!" came the shouts again. "H – ELLLLLL – PPPPP!"

"Good gracious!" puffed the engine. "We'd better go and see what's happening. That sounds like the little family of pixies who live down the old rabbit hole. They're so nice. Who'll come with me to rescue them?"

"I'm too little," said the clockwork mouse.

"I'm too fat," said the teddy bear.

"I'm too frightened," said the golden-haired doll.

"My clockwork's run down," said the clockwork clown.

"Well, dear me – I'm the only one left to go!" said the pink rabbit. "I don't want to – I'm scared. But I suppose I must."

"Of course you must," puffed the engine. "Get into my cab and drive me. Go on – quickly!"

The pink rabbit climbed into the cab and drove the train down the garden path – bumpity-bumpity-bump! He came to the end of it and ran the train over the lawn. Soon they arrived at the hedge where the rabbit hole was – and will you believe it, those wicked little red imps, no bigger than fieldmice, had caught all the pretty little pixies and tied them up!

"Listen," puffed the engine quietly, "tell the red imps I'll give them a ride round the garden for a treat. You stay here with the pixies, and undo their ropes."

"No," said the pink rabbit angrily. "I won't have you giving those bad red imps a treat like that."

"Do as you're told," said the engine, puffing so hard that the pink rabbit fell over.

He went to the red imps sulkily. "The engine says it will give you a ride round the garden if you like," he said.

"Oooooh! Come on, then!" cried the biggest imp, and ran to the carriages. "I've always wanted a ride in a train. Don't you try to untie those pixies, Rabbit – if you do, we'll tie *you* up, and throw you into a prickly rose bush!"

They were soon sitting in the wooden carriages of the little train. What fun! The imps leaned over the sides and laughed excitedly. A ride in a train! Well, what a surprise! The biggest one called out to the frightened pixies.

"You stay there till we come back. You can't run far, anyway!"

Rumble-rumble-rumble! Away went the wooden train round the garden, the imps squeaking in delight. The pink rabbit frowned after it. "Horrid train – being so nice to the bad red imps! Well – I must try and undo these knots, and set the poor little pixies free. But I *am* so bad at knots!"

"Just undo *mine*," said a small pixie with a silvery dress that shone in the moonlight. "Then I can undo all the others. My fingers are small, you see – yours are so large and clumsy, Rabbit. Just undo *my* knots! Hurry!"

"Good idea," said the pink rabbit, and began to undo the knots that tied up the little pixie. His fingers were large and the knots were small – but at last he had them all undone, and the pixie gave a cry of delight.

"Good! Thank you very much. Now I'll undo the others. Oh dear, I do hope

the train doesn't come back yet! I don't want to be tied up all over again!"

She ran to her friends, and tugged at their knots – and then, alas, the pink rabbit heard the train puffing back again!

"Ha-ha-ha!" it puffed. "He-he-he! Ho-ho-ho!"

"It sounds as if it's laughing," said the pink rabbit, in disgust. "Surely it isn't happy because it's taking those horrid red imps for a ride!"

The wooden train ran up, bumpity-bump, still chuckling. Well, what a surprise – all the carriages were empty!

"Where are those imps?" asked the pink rabbit, astonished.

"Well, you didn't *really* think I was being kind and giving those red imps a treat, did you?" said the engine. "Of course not! I ran them down the garden path, straight to the little pond. And then I ran right into the water, and in they fell with such a splash! *I* floated, of course, because I'm wooden, and I soon

25

got out again – but the imps are still there!"

"What – in the pond?" cried the rabbit in delight.

"Yes. Some are sitting shivering on the lily-leaves, some are being chased by a big frog, and the others are spluttering and yelling!" said the engine, giving a sudden giggle. "But they'll soon find their way out of the water – so for goodness sake tell the pixies to get into my carriages, and I'll take them safely to the playroom at once. They can spend the night in the dolls' house."

The pixies climbed up the creeper with the pink rabbit to help them. The teddy bear and the others were there to help too. They made a great fuss of the pink rabbit who really felt quite a hero!

And now the tiny pixies are all fast asleep in the dolls' house very comfortable indeed. The pink rabbit has locked the door, in case the red imps come back.

But they won't. They've all gone

home, wet through, to dry their clothes! "Oh that rabbit!" said the biggest one. "Telling us to have a ride in that horrid train. Just wait till we meet him again! We'll soon find those pixies and tie them up even more tightly!"

But they won't find them, because a strange thing has happened. The pink rabbit has lost the key to the front door of the dolls' house! So the pixies can't get out and are still living there happily, very, very pleased to have such a nice home!

But I can't think what Jean and Donald will say when they play with the dolls' house next week – and see the little pixie family living so happily in its four small rooms!

Jane goes out to stay

Jane was going to stay with her friend Pam. She felt very grown-up indeed. She had never been away from home before – but here she was, watching Mummy pack a little bag with her nightdress and dressing-gown, her flannel, sponge and toothbrush, and a clean dress.

"Shall I pack Bunny for you?" said Mummy.

"Oh, *no*," said Jane. "I know he sleeps with me every night, Mummy, but I'm too big to take a bunny away with me. Pam would laugh at me."

"No, she wouldn't. Pam is a year younger than you are, and I expect she takes a toy to bed with her every

single night," said Mummy. "Very well. I won't put Bunny in."

Jane thought of all the things she would tell Pam. She wanted to make Pam think she was very grown-up and important. She would say, "Pam, do you know this – Pam, do you know that?" and Pam would listen eagerly.

She arrived at Pam's in time for dinner. Pam hugged her, because she liked Jane very much.

"Do you mind being away from home?" she said. "Will you like staying with me? I've never stayed away even one night without Mummy."

"Ah, but I'm older than you," said Jane. "I'm in a class higher at school, too. I shan't mind staying away from home a bit!"

They had dinner, and then they went out to play. The dog next door barked, and made Pam jump.

"Are you afraid of dogs?" said Jane. "I've got a dog of my own at home. Can you ride?"

"No, I can't. Can you?" asked Pam.

"Oh, yes. I ride every Saturday, on a big, white pony called Sweetie," said Jane. "I gallop. And once I went so fast that everyone thought my pony was running away. But he wasn't."

"You must be very clever," said Pam. "I wish I could do things like that."

Jane chose all the games, and she chose ones she was quite the best in. She could run faster than Pam, and she could jump higher.

"Mummy, Jane is wonderful," said Pam, when they went in to tea. "She does everything so well. And she's not a bit afraid of dogs or horses – or of tigers, either, are you, Jane?"

"I don't expect I would be, if I met one," said Jane, pleased at all this praise. "I like animals. You ought to like animals, too, Pam, then you wouldn't be so scared when you see a big dog, or hear a cow moo."

After tea they played card games. Jane was much quicker at them than

Pam. She 'Snapped' everything, and won four games straight off. Pam looked a little sad.

"I wish I could win once," she said.

"Have a game of Happy Families. You may win then," said her mother, feeling rather sorry for the smaller girl. She thought that Jane might just let Pam win once, to please her. But no, Jane won Happy Families, too.

"I'm stupid, aren't I?" said poor Pam, almost in tears. "I wish I was as wonderful as Jane, Mummy. She can do everything. Jane, do you ever cry?"

"Oh, no," said Jane. But this wasn't quite true. She did cry sometimes.

"Not even when you fall down and hurt your knee?" asked Pam.

"Of *course* not!" said Jane.

"Are you ever frightened in the night?" said Pam. "Because I am."

"Of *course* I'm not," said Jane, in a scornful voice. "I just go to sleep, and don't bother about anything, not even thunder."

"You're too good to be true, Jane, dear," said Pam's Mummy. "And now I think it's bedtime. Hurry up and have a nice hot bath, because it's very cold tonight."

Soon the two little girls were in separate little beds, drinking a nice warm glass of milk. Then Pam's mother said good night to them both, and went downstairs.

She came up a little later with Pam's hot water bottle, and one for Jane, too. But Jane was already fast asleep. So very gently Pam's mother pushed the hot water bottle, in its soft furry cover, down into the bed beside the sleeping Jane. Jane never had a hot water bottle at home, and had not asked for one.

About three hours later Jane woke up. She felt a warm patch against her legs. Whatever could it be? She put down her hand and felt it. It was soft and furry and warm. It must be some animal that had crept into bed with her when she was asleep!

"Go away!" said Jane, and kicked out at it. But it didn't move. It just lay against her leg, furry and warm. Jane felt suddenly frightened.

She sat up in bed and shouted. "Help! Help! There's a wild animal in bed with me! It's biting me, it's biting me, help, help!"

Pam woke up with a jump. She switched on the light and stared at Jane. "Oh, Pam! There's a horrid wild animal in bed with me!" cried Jane again. "It'll bite me to bits! I believe it's nibbling me now! Oh! OHHHHH!"

"I'll save you, I'll save you!" cried Pam, and she jumped out of bed. She pulled Jane right out of bed, and then threw back the covers. She saw the furry hot water bottle cover, and bent to pick it up and throw it away, thinking it was some animal.

Then she saw what it was. How she stared! Then she laughed. She had a very merry little laugh, that went ha-ha-ha-ho-ho-ho, he-he. She rolled on

Jane's bed and she laughed till the tears came into her eyes.

"What's the matter, Pam?" asked Jane, upset. But Pam was laughing too much to tell her. Then in came Pam's mother to see what all the noise was about.

"Oh, Mummy, oh, Mummy! Jane was so funny!" said Pam. "She screamed and shouted and cried because she said she had a wild animal in her bed that was biting her to bits! And I got out to rescue her from the dreadful animal – and it was only her hot water bottle!"

Then it was Mummy's turn to laugh. "Well, well, well – to think of our brave and wonderful Jane being scared of a hot water bottle! I slipped it into your bed, dear, when you were asleep."

Poor Jane! She did feel so very, very silly. To think she had yelled like that over a hot water bottle.

She got back into bed, very red in the face. She threw the hot water bottle out on the floor.

"Now don't be cross as well as foolish, Jane," said Pam's mother. "It really was very funny, you know, and we couldn't help laughing. And don't you think little Pam was brave, to jump out of bed and come and try to save you from the wild animal you were shouting about?"

"Yes. She was brave," said Jane. "Thank you, Pam. You're braver than I am!"

Then they went to sleep. But you won't be surprised to hear that next day Jane was much nicer to Pam, and even let her win two games of Snap!

The winter wide-awakes

Mummy put her head in at the playroom door and saw a very cosy scene. There was a big fire burning, and three children were sitting by it. Two were playing a game of Snap, and the other was reading.

"Do you know who's here?" she said. "Auntie Lou."

"Oh!" said all three children, raising their heads. They were Tessie, Pat and Johnny. Tessie looked a little doubtful.

"I hope she hasn't come to take us for a walk," she said. "Auntie Lou is lovely to go for walks with in the summer, but it's all snowy outside now and very cold. I don't think I want to go out today."

Another head came round the door.

It belonged to Auntie Lou. She was dressed in warm tweeds and had a bright red scarf round her neck. Her head was bare, and her cheeks were as red as her scarf. Her blue eyes twinkled.

"What's this I hear? You don't want to go out with me? Well, I like that! Who came and begged to go out with me every week in the summer? Who went to find conkers and nuts and blackberries with me in the autumn because I knew all the best places?"

"We did," said Pat with a grin. "But, Auntie Lou, we're so warm and cosy here, and there's nothing to see in the country now. Honestly there isn't."

"There's nothing but snow," said Johnny, "and all the birds are gone, and all the animals are asleep."

"What a poor little ignorant boy!" said Auntie Lou, making a funny face. "It's true we shouldn't see anything of the winter sleepers – they're all tucked away in their holes – but we could see plenty of wide-awakes."

"Who are they?" asked Johnny.

"Well, as I came over the fields this morning to pay a call on three lazy children, I saw a beautiful red fox," said Auntie Lou. "He wasn't asleep. He almost bumped into me coming round the hedge. I didn't hear him and I suppose he didn't hear me."

"Oh, a fox!" said Pat. "I'd like to have seen that. Auntie, I'll come with you if you'll show me all the wide-awakes."

"We'll all come," said Tessie, shutting her book. "I'd like to find some wide-awakes too, and some birds as well. Lots have gone away, but we've still plenty left, haven't we, Auntie?"

"Plenty," said her aunt. "Hurry up, then. I'll give you three minutes to put on boots and coats."

They were all ready quickly, for they knew perfectly well that Auntie Lou wouldn't wait for anyone who wasn't. They set off down the snowy garden path.

"You can see how many birds have

been in your garden this morning," said Auntie Lou, pointing to some bird-tracks in the snow. "Look, that's where the sparrows have been. See the little footmarks all set out in pairs? That's because they hop with their feet together. And there are the marks of a running bird – his footmarks are behind one another."

Johnny hopped with his feet together, and then ran. He saw that he had left his first footmarks in pairs, but the other marks were spread out behind one another. Auntie Lou laughed. "The footmarks of the Johnny-Bird," she said.

By the frozen pond they came to other bird-prints, and Tessie pointed to them. "Ducks," she said. "You can see the marks of the webbing between their toes."

"Yes. The poor things thought they might have a swim on the pond, and came waddling up from the farm to see," said Auntie Lou. "I wonder what they think when they find they can't splash in the ice."

They left the pond behind and struck across the fields. How lovely they were, all blanketed in snow! The hedges were sprinkled with snow too, but here and there the red hips showed and the green, unripe ivy-berries.

"Look, Auntie," said Pat, pointing to some bark in the hedgerow which had been gnawed white. "Who's been doing that? Somebody must have been very hungry to eat bark."

"One of the most wide-awakes," said Auntie Lou. She pointed to some tracks. "Look, rabbit footmarks. The bunnies have been gnawing bark because they are so hungry."

"But why don't they eat the grass?" said Tessie. The two boys laughed at her.

"How can they when it's deep down under the snow?" said Pat scornfully. "Use your brains, Tessie!"

"Oh, I never thought of that," said

Tessie. "Poor little rabbits – they must get awfully hungry when their grass is hidden away. No wonder they come and gnaw at the bark."

"Yes, and the fox knows they will come out to feed somewhere," said Auntie Lou. "So he comes out too, and pads along quietly in the snow, watching for an unwary rabbit. I saw a sad little scattering of grey fur this morning as I came along, to show me where the fox had made his breakfast."

"Look, what's that?" suddenly whispered Johnny, clutching at his aunt's arm. She looked where he was pointing.

"A stoat," she said. "He's after the rabbits, I expect."

"But he's white," said Johnny, amazed. "He wasn't white when we saw him in the summer."

"Ah, he's clever. He changed his dark coat for a white one in the winter when the snow came," said his aunt; "all but the tip of his tail, which is black. Now his enemies can't see him against the white snow."

"Isn't he clever?" said Pat. "He's cleverer than the fox. *He* doesn't change his red coat to white. Does the stoat always change his coat, Auntie Lou?"

"Only in cold climates," said his aunt, "not down in the south where it is warmer and there is little snow in the winter. Now look, what's that?"

"A weasel," said Pat. "He's wide awake too, isn't he? Look at him, going along almost like a slinky snake."

They went by another farm. The farmer was standing at the door of his cow-shed and hailed them.

"Good morning. It's a fine morning for a walk, isn't it? It's a pity I can't send my cows out for a walk too. They're tired of standing in their sheds."

"Farmer Toms, have you lots of mice and rats about?" asked Johnny. "We're out looking for wide-awake creatures today, and we've seen plenty; but we've seen no rats nor mice."

"Ah, I've too many – far too many," said the farmer. "Up in the loft there, where I store my grain, I get no end of the creatures. You go up and maybe you'll see some."

They all climbed the ladder and went into the dark loft. They sat down on sacks and kept quiet. Almost at once they heard a squeaking. Then two mice appeared from a hole and scampered over to a bin.

"There are two," called Tessie, but her voice frightened them of course, and they turned to run away; then a rat suddenly appeared and made a dart at one of the mice. Tessie gave a squeal.

"Oh! A rat! Horrid, sharp-nosed thing! Auntie, I don't like rats. Let's go down."

The mice disappeared, and the rat slunk away too. He was a thin rat and looked very hungry. Perhaps he wasn't very clever at catching mice. Nobody liked the look of him.

"The rat is every animal's enemy, and ours as well," said Auntie Lou. "I haven't anything good to say of him."

The mice squealed behind the boards. "They are saying, 'Hear, hear,'" said Pat, and that made everyone laugh.

They went down the ladder and told Farmer Toms what they had seen. Then they went into the shed. The cows smelt nice and turned their big heads to look at the children.

"Where are your sheep?" asked Johnny.

The farmer waved his hand up to the hills. "Away up there in the snow with the shepherd," he said. "He's got them safe and is expecting their little lambs soon. They're often born in the snowy weather, and they're none the worse for it. You must go and see them when they are born."

The children left the farm and went on their way.

"I wouldn't have believed there was so much to see on a snowy wintry day," said Tessie. "I really wouldn't. Why, it's as interesting as summer-time."

"Look, there's a thrush – and a blackbird too – eating the hips in the snowy hedge," said Pat. "Aren't they enjoying themselves? What a good thing there are berries to feed the hungry birds in the winter!"

"And look at all those chaffinches," said Tessie, as a flock of the bright little birds flew over her head towards the farm. "I've never seen so many chaffinches together before."

"No, in the spring and summer they go about in pairs," said her aunt. "But many birds in winter like to flock together. They are probably going to see if there is any grain round about the farm for them to peck up. Look up into the sky – you'll see some other birds there that flock by the thousand."

"Peewits!" said Johnny. "Don't their wings twinkle as they fly? I do love their call too – just like their name!"

"I should think we've seen all the winter wide-awakes now," said Tessie. But Auntie Lou shook her head.

"No, there's another. I saw him this morning as I came through the hazel wood. He *has* been asleep, but this lovely sunny day woke him up. He doesn't mind the snow a bit. Look, there he is, the pretty thing!"

A squirrel suddenly bounded down a tree trunk and ran right over to the children. Auntie Lou put her hand in her pocket and took out a few shelled nuts. "Here you are," she said to the amusing little squirrel. "I've shelled them for you, so you won't have any bother today."

The squirrel took a nut from her fingers, skipped away a few paces, then sat up with the nut in his paws and began to eat it quickly. The children watched him in delight.

"He's a great friend of mine," said Auntie Lou. "If he's awake and I walk through his wood, he always comes along to me to see if I've anything for him. I expect he has plenty of nuts and acorns hidden away, but he does love a

49

peanut or brazil nut already shelled for him – it makes a change from his own nuts."

"Let's take him home! Oh, do let's take him home!" said Johnny, and he tried to catch the bushy-tailed squirrel; but in a trice the little creature ran up a nearby trunk, his tail out behind him, and sat high above their heads, making a little chattering noise.

"His home is up in that tree," said Auntie Lou. "I've no doubt he has a very cosy hole there, safe from little boys who want to take him home with them."

"Oh, I do like him," said Johnny. "Perhaps in the spring, when he has tiny young squirrel children, I could have one of those. I'd love a squirrel-pet. I'd call him Scamper."

The squirrel disappeared into his home. Auntie Lou began to walk through the trees. "It's time we went home too," she said. "Look how the sun is sinking. It will soon be getting dark. Come along."

They ran after her, looking about for more squirrels, but they saw none. Johnny made up his mind to go to the woods the very next day and make friends with the little squirrel all by himself.

"He's the nicest winter wide-awake we've seen," he said. "What a lot we've met today, Auntie! I'd no idea there were so many birds and animals to see on such a wintry day."

It began to get dark. "We shan't see any more now," said Tessie. But they did! As they walked down the lane home, a little bird kept pace with them, flying from tree to tree as they went, giving them little bursts of song.

"It's a robin," said Auntie Lou. "He is always the latest bird to go to bed. Maybe he's the one that belongs to your garden, children. Look out for him tomorrow, and scatter some crumbs for him."

"We will," said Tessie, opening the garden gate. The robin flew in before her. "Yes, he must be ours. He has come to welcome us home. Auntie, you're coming in to tea, aren't you?"

"Of course," said Auntie Lou. "I think I deserve a very nice tea, with hot scones and homemade jam, after taking you three children out to see so many wide-awakes."

"You do! You do!" chorused the children. And she did, didn't she? I hope you'll see a lot of wide-awakes if *you* go out on a winter's day.

"It's my birthday"

Jib the brownie hadn't a proper house. He lived in a snug little tent that he had made out of the big leaves of the chestnut tree. He just sewed them together and, lo and behold, he had a nice little tent.

He used to live for a few days in one place and then roll up his tent, tie it on his back and go off to another village. And in every place he pitched his tent, he would say the same thing.

"It's my birthday tomorrow!"

Then he would sigh and look sad, and the people round him would say, "Why do you look sad?"

And Jib would say, "Well, it's sad to be away from home and my friends and have a birthday – no presents, no cards, nothing!"

Well, the pixies and elves were kind little people and you can guess what they did!

"Let's go and buy Jib birthday cards and some little presents!" they would say, and off they would go at once.

And the next day Jib would have lovely cards and all kinds of nice little presents. The little folk would beam at him and wonder if he would give a birthday party and ask them all to it.

But he never did. On that very afternoon he would quietly fold up his chestnut-leaf tent and steal away; and when a pixie came by, no Jib and no tent were there! That was really very mean of him.

One day he came to the village of Ho. It was full of brownies like himself, and pixies and elves. Jib put up his little tent, and people came to call.

"My name's Jib," he said. "I hope you don't mind my staying here in my tent.

It seems such a nice place and such nice people."

"Oh, we like to make strangers welcome," said Boff, a big, burly brownie with a very long beard. "We hope you'll be happy here."

Jib hung his head and looked sad. "I expect I *shall* be happy soon," he said, "but just now I feel rather miserable. You see – it's my birthday tomorrow – and it's sad to be far from home and have no cards and no presents."

"Dear me – we must do something about *that*," said kind Mrs Boff. She and Boff went off, talking together, and Jib grinned to himself. Now he would have plenty of cards and heaps of presents.

"I shall leave tomorrow afternoon, and go to Cherry Village and sell all the presents," he said to himself. "I shall get a nice lot of money for them. How very stupid people are, to be sure!"

Mr and Mrs Boff went round the village of Ho, telling everyone that Jib was having a birthday the next day and people must try and make it nice for him.

"Hm!" said Old Wily the goblin. "I don't much like the look of that fellow, Jib. Why should we spend money on him? Would he spend any on us?"

"Oh, he's sure to have a little party and ask us all to it," said Mrs Boff. "He'll be so pleased with his cards and presents, he'll surely want to do something nice in return."

Old Wily didn't think that a brownie with a mean face like Jib's would ever want to do anything nice for anyone. He sat and thought for a little while, and then he put on his old hat and went to visit his cousin, Old Sly. There wasn't much that Old Sly didn't know. He had lived a long time and he had heard a lot and knew a lot. He was two hundred years old and his beard had grown down to his feet and round his ankles.

"Ever heard of anyone called Jib?" asked Old Wily.

Old Sly frowned and thought for a

long while. "Ah, yes," he said at last. "He's the fellow who goes round with a chestnut-leaf tent and says he's miserable because it's his birthday and he's far from home. Then he collects a whole lot of presents and sells them in the next village. A very unpleasant fellow."

"Thank you, Old Sly," said Old Wily. "Exactly what I thought." Off he went back to the village of Ho, thinking hard. He found that everyone had bought a card or a present for Jib.

Old Wily went to visit the baker. "It's Mr Jib's birthday tomorrow," he said. "And he wants to have a nice little party. Will you arrange it, please? Birthday cake and buns and sandwiches and ice-creams and biscuits and jellies and balloons and crackers. All the very best, of course."

"Certainly, certainly," said the baker, delighted, and he set to work.

Well, next day Jib sat in his tent and waited for the little folk to bring him cards and presents. And as usual they did! Dear me, what a lot of money they had spent on that rascal Jib.

"*So* kind of you!" he kept saying. "So very kind! Thank you, thank you!"

"He hasn't said anything about a party yet," whispered Mrs Boff.

"Oh, there'll be a party," said Old Wily. "Yes, yes – there's sure to be a party. A fine one, too. I've seen the baker icing a splendid birthday cake."

Well, Jib heard this, as Old Wily meant that he should, and he was delighted. "What! A party as well as all these presents," he thought. "Magnificent!"

So he didn't fold up his chestnut-leaf tent and steal away as he usually did. He waited for the party!

It was a very fine party indeed. The birthday cake was made in the shape of a white palace and really looked lovely. Everyone had two pieces. Jib had three, and goodness knows how many cakes and buns and ice-creams he had as well.

And after the party, when everyone was saying goodbye, the baker came up and bowed. "I hope everything was all right, Mr Jib," he said.

"Perfectly," said Jib. "Couldn't be better."

"I'm glad," said the baker and unrolled a long sheet of paper. "Here's the bill."

What a bill it was! Jib stared in horror. What! All that money for a party. Well, *he* wasn't going to pay for it!

"I'm not paying that," he said, roughly.

"But it was *your* birthday party!" said Old Wily, who had put himself nearby. "Surely you gave it in return for the kindness of all these people? Surely, Jib, you didn't mean to fold up your tent and go without paying the bill? Oh, surely not! Where is Mr Plod the policeman? Let us ask him if that would be a right thing to do."

Jib looked very scared. He didn't like

policemen. He was always afraid they would find out all his mean little tricks. He hurriedly put his hand into his pocket, and pulled out a very fat purse. He paid the baker's bill without a word.

"That was wise of you, Jib, very wise," said Old Wily. "I hope you will *always* pay for birthday parties on the many birthdays you have each year. Will you, Jib?"

Jib began to tremble. He waited till everyone had gone then he packed up his tent quickly. Old Wily watched him go. "I'm coming to your next birthday party!" he called. "Let me see now — when is your next birthday, Jib? Next week, I suppose. I'll be there!"

Jib went hurrying off without a word, and so far as I know he hasn't had a birthday since! What a way to go on, wasn't it?

A tale about Tumpy

I must tell you a tale about Tumpy and his caravan. He and Mr Spells shared it with Bits the dog. It was a most unusual caravan because it had feet instead of wheels, and it could walk for miles, taking Tumpy, Mr Spells and Bits with it.

Now one day Tumpy looked at the caravan curtains and he saw that they were very dirty. "Look here, Spells," he said, "just look at these curtains! You must wash them!"

"Good gracious, no!" said Spells, alarmed. "I couldn't possibly wash big things like these. You wash them yourself!"

"Oh, well," said Tumpy, "we'll send

them to the washerwoman in the next village – what's her name now – Mrs Suds."

"All right. I'll take them down and

pack them into the basket," said Spells. "Hey, Bits – come and hold the ladder for me!" Bits the dog helped all he could. Mr Spells took down the curtains, sneezing because of the dust in them. They were the winter curtains, nice warm velvet ones. Spells popped them all into the big basket.

Then he went out to do some shopping. "You mind the caravan while we shop," he told Bits, and off went Tumpy and Spells together.

Bits the dog was bored. He tried to find a comfortable place to lie in, but he couldn't. He wasn't allowed on the beds, and Tumpy had hung all the rugs out on a line outside, ready to beat them when he came back. Bits felt cross.

Then he saw the basket of velvet curtains. Ah! they looked comfortable and soft and warm. Tumpy and Spells wouldn't be back for some time. He could hop into the basket, snuggle between the curtains there and have a good sleep.

So Bits jumped in, snuggled on the velvet curtains, put his nose on his paws, and fell asleep. He was still asleep when Tumpy and Spells came back. They were in a hurry.

"What a bit of luck that we met the washerwoman!" said Tumpy. "Now she can take the curtains home with her and we can call for them on our way back in the caravan."

Mrs Suds was a big, strong woman. She could carry the basket on her shoulders easily. Tumpy shut down the lid, and fastened it. He gave it to Mrs Suds and watched her stagger off with it.

"I wouldn't have thought that curtains weighed so heavily," said Tumpy to Spells. "Well, let's go on our way, Spells. Hey, Caravan – put your best foot forward! Off we go again!"

The caravan set off. It hadn't gone very far before Tumpy realized Bits the dog was missing. "Where's Bits?" he said, looking in every corner of the caravan. "Hey, Bits! BITS! Where are you? Now, where's that dog gone?"

"Stop, Caravan, stop!" called Spells. "We've lost Bits." But the caravan didn't stop. It was enjoying a walk after its rest. It went a bit faster.

"Caravan! Do as you're told!" shouted Tumpy. "You are most disobedient today. Stop, I say!"

But the caravan began to run, and Tumpy sat down very suddenly. Things began to slide around inside the van.

"We'd better get out and try and find Bits," said Spells, anxiously. But Tumpy shook his head.

"No. With the caravan in this silly sort of mood we'll be left behind, Spells. Goodness knows where it will run to! We might lose it altogether. Oh, dear — where in the world can Bits be?"

Well, the caravan ran on all that day and all that night. "It's gone right past the washerwoman's village," said Spells, gloomily. "Now we shall lose our curtains, too. Really, this caravan wants a good telling off. Trotting on and on like this. What behaviour!"

Well, very fortunately, the caravan got a bit tired, so at the next village it came to, it stopped. Tumpy and Spells were very glad. They said a lot of furious things to the caravan, and then wondered what to do about looking for poor Bits. Where *could* he have got to?

"Hello! Who's this coming panting up to us?" said Tumpy, suddenly. "It looks like Mr Suds, the washerwoman's husband. And he's got our washing basket on his shoulder. Oh, good – Mrs Suds must have done the curtains."

It *was* Mr Suds. He set the basket down and gave Tumpy a bill. Tumpy stared in surprise.

"For washing three pairs velvet curtains, very dirty – three pounds.

"For washing one dog, also very dirty, fifty pence."

"Dog! – what dog?" said Tumpy, astonished. "We didn't send a dog to be washed."

"Yes, you did," said Mr Suds. "He was in the basket too. So Mrs Suds washed him and you won't know him, he's so clean. She's popped him into a paper bag, and he's in with the curtains."

Tumpy opened the lid of the basket – and out leapt poor Bits, looking so clean that Tumpy and Spells really didn't know him! He jumped up at them, and licked them till they were quite wet.

"Oh, Bits! You must have put yourself into the basket and got taken away to be washed!" said Tumpy, patting him. "How silly you are! Don't you do such a stupid thing again!"

"He won't," said Mr Suds. "He didn't like being washed at all. It's a good thing Mrs Suds didn't iron him like the curtains."

"Woof," said poor Bits, with his tail down. What a fuss Spells and Tumpy made of him that day! And will you believe it, the very first chance Bits had, he went and rolled himself in some mud. What a waste of fifty pence!

The tale of Twisty and Ho-Ho

O nce upon a time Ho-Ho the Goblin went along by the fields to catch the bus that went to the market. He walked by the stream and sang as he walked, for it was a very pleasant day.

Ho-Ho was going to buy some cows for his master. He was to bring them home that evening. He had cut himself a big stick from the hedge, and with this he meant to drive the cows home. Ah, Ho-Ho felt very important today! He stood still for a moment and looked at the bubbling stream.

"The cows shall drink out of this stream," he said. "They will be thirsty, walking all the way home this hot day."

Now, as Ho-Ho stood watching the

sparkling water, he heard the sound of someone whistling, and he turned round to see who was coming. He saw Twisty the gnome coming along swinging a big stick as he went.

"Good morning, Twisty!" called Ho-Ho. "Where are you going?"

"I am going to the market to buy my master some sheep," said Twisty, "and this is the stick I have cut to drive them home!"

"Now that is a funny thing," cried Ho-Ho. "I am going to the market to buy my master some good cows that will be sold there today. And I have cut this stick to drive them home! We will catch the bus together, buy our animals together, and come home together!"

"Yes," said Twisty. "And my master said to me, 'Twisty,' he said, 'see that you give the sheep a drink on the way home, for they will be very thirsty walking so far on the dusty roads.' When I saw this stream I thought that this would be where they drank."

"No," said Ho-Ho at once. "They cannot drink here, Twisty."

"And why not?" asked Twisty.

"Because my cows will drink here tonight," said Ho-Ho. "And they will be very thirsty indeed, and will drink so much that there will be none left for your sheep."

"Then you must take your cows somewhere else to drink," said Twisty. "For certainly my sheep will drink here! I will not have your cows drinking from this stream, for, if they do, there will not be enough water for my sheep!"

"I tell you your sheep shall *not* drink here!" shouted Ho-Ho.

"And I tell you that your cows shall not drink here!" Twisty shouted back.

Ho-Ho banged his stick on the ground, and the dust flew up. "If you bring your sheep to this field, and let them drink from this stream, I shall drive them away," he said.

Twisty hammered his stick on the ground, and the dust flew up in such a cloud that Ho-Ho began to choke. "I tell you, Ho-Ho, if you bring your cows here tonight I shall push them all into the water!" shouted Twisty.

"Indeed you will not!" yelled Ho-Ho.

With that he struck out at Twisty with his stick. The gnome lifted his own stick and hit out at Ho-Ho. He knocked his hat off, and it fell into the water.

"There goes my best hat!" groaned Ho-Ho, and he stamped on the ground in rage. He poked Twisty hard with his stick, and the gnome over-balanced and fell splash into the stream!

He sat up in the water and shook his fist at Ho-Ho, who was standing on the bank laughing loudly. Out of the water jumped Twisty, shook himself like a dog, and jumped at Ho-Ho. Over and over on the grass they rolled, and at last down the bank of the stream they went together, *splish-splash* into the water. How they choked and spluttered as they lay in the water trying to get out!

"I've swallowed a fish!" said Twisty.

"I've swallowed two!" said Ho-Ho. "And see how wet I am!"

"So am I," said Twisty. "Let us get out and dry our clothes before we go to market. It will never do to go to market dripping wet."

So they climbed out of the stream and sat on the grass in the sun. They took off their coats and hung them on a tree nearby to dry.

And, as they sat there, drying, they heard on the road not far off the *rumble-rumble-rumble* of the bus. It was on its way to market, the only bus of the morning!

"The bus! The bus!" shouted Twisty, and he jumped to his feet. "Come, quickly, Ho-Ho, or we shall miss it."

They tore off over the field and came to the gate as the bus passed. It stopped when the driver saw them, and the two ran to it; but even as they took hold of the rail to pull themselves into the bus they remembered something.

Their coats! They had left them drying on the tree – and in the pockets of their coats was the money their masters had given them to buy the cows and the sheep! They could not go to market to buy without money.

"Wait a moment for us," begged Twisty. "We have left our coats in the field."

The gnome and the goblin raced over the field and took down their wet coats.

They turned to go back to the waiting bus, and Twisty said: "Well now, just you remember, Ho-Ho, on no account are you to bring your cows here tonight to drink from my sheep's stream!"

"What do you mean?" shouted Ho-Ho. "I told you I had chosen it for my cows, and that you were not to bring your sheep!"

Just as they stood glaring at one another they heard a *rumble-rumble-rumble* – and the bus had gone on down the lane! It would not wait any longer, for it was already late. It had gone, and the two quarrellers were left behind.

They stared at the disappearing bus in dismay. It climbed the hill and went over the top. They could not get to market that morning.

"I shall have no cows to bring to the stream to drink," said Ho-Ho, in a small voice, "and my master will be very angry with me."

"And I shall have no sheep to bring to the stream to drink," said Twisty, "and my master will be so angry with me that I shall have no dinner and no supper."

"Why did we quarrel?" said Ho-Ho. "The stream is big enough to give water to all the sheep and cows in the market!"

"We were selfish!" cried Twisty. "We each wanted the whole stream for our animals, and now we have no animals to bring to the stream. It serves us right. Goodbye, Ho-Ho. I am going to tell my master that I have missed the bus."

"Goodbye," said Ho-Ho. "I must go back to the farm, too. Next time we meet, Twisty, we will be more sensible."

The flyaway balloon

Auntie Mary gave a New Year's party to all her nieces and nephews. It was a very nice party with heaps of crackers, balloons and things to eat.

There was one balloon that had somehow got blown up much bigger than the others. It floated with them in a great big bunch, each balloon on its own string. It was very pleased with itself.

"How big I am!" it thought. "How very, very big! Much bigger than the others. I am a giant balloon, and if I had a long enough string I could fly up to that big balloon in the sky – what's it called, now? Oh, yes, the moon. I am sure I must be as big as the moon."

It wondered which child would have it. Auntie Mary wondered, too. It was such a lovely big blue balloon, with such a nice smiley face on it that she thought it really ought to be a prize for something.

"I'll give it as a prize for musical chairs," she thought. "Whoever wins musical chairs shall have that big balloon!"

Alice won it. She was very pleased. She took the great big balloon from her aunt and held it in her arms, squashing its firm softness against her.

"It feels lovely," she said. "It's a giant balloon. It will never, never burst!"

"Burst! Whatever does she mean?" thought the big balloon. "Why should I burst? I never, never will."

And then suddenly there was a loud POP near by. Somebody else's balloon had burst. All the children jumped, and so did the balloons. What a horrid noise! And where had that balloon gone? One minute it was a lovely big yellow thing – the next it had disappeared, and all that was to be seen was a tiny bit of dirty-looking rubber, torn and ragged, tied to the string.

The big balloon was alarmed. Was that what bursting meant? It didn't like the sound of it at all! Alice flung her big balloon into the air, holding it by its short string.

"Look – look! See how this enormous balloon flies!" she cried. "Isn't it a beauty! I'm sure it would fly like a kite if I had a long enough string and took it out in the wind."

The big balloon tried to reach the ceiling but it couldn't. The string held it back. Horrid string! The balloon wished it could get away from it.

Alice took the big balloon home. She hung it up in her bedroom at the end of the bed. The wind came in at the window and played with it, bobbing it about to and fro. It liked that.

The next day Alice took the big

balloon out in the wind on its string. Aha! The wind had a wonderful game with it, and blew it quite high in the air. But the string always pulled it back.

"I might be a dog on a lead, instead of a beautiful balloon that wants to fly up to the moon," thought the balloon, angrily. "Why doesn't Alice get me a longer string? Oh, I wish I could fly high!"

And then, next time the wind blew strongly, the balloon jerked so hard at the string that it slipped out of Alice's fingers – and the balloon at once shot high up into the air, far above the trees!

"I'm free, I'm free!" it thought, and its smiling face looked down on Alice. But the little girl was very upset. She began to cry. "You've gone! You were the biggest balloon I ever had – and now you've gone! You'll bump into something and burst. Oh, do, do be careful, balloon – don't bump into anything sharp!"

The balloon floated higher and

higher. It wanted to go to the clouds.
Were they a kind of white balloon, too?
And where was that moon? That should
surely be hanging in the sky like a big
silver balloon. Perhaps it would come
when it was dark, and then the big
balloon could fly up to it, and talk to
it. It was sure it would be bigger than
the moon!

The wind dropped. The balloon fell
nearer to earth. Down, down, down. It
came near to a tree. Be careful, balloon
– that's a holly tree. BE CAREFUL! It
is set with sharp prickles! You'll burst –
you'll go POP!

A robin sang out sharply: "Go away!
You'll go pop-bang! Go away!"

The balloon swerved away from the
holly tree. Oh dear – what a narrow
escape! What dreadfully sharp prickles
it had nearly floated into.

It fell lower still. A sparrow chirruped
loudly. "Balloon, be careful! That's
barbed wire! It's set with sharp points.
It will prick you and you'll BURST.

You'll go POP and we shan't see you any more!"

The balloon just missed the barbed wire. It was so alarmed that its smiling face didn't smile any more. It began to wish it was with Alice, on a nice short, safe string!

It fell to the ground and floated along, bumping up and down as it went. A rabbit saw it and ran after it, hitting it with its paw.

"Don't! You'll burst me!" cried the balloon in a squeaky, rubbery voice. The wind took it up into the air out of the rabbit's reach – but then down it fell again to the ground. This time it fell near a farm.

Two hens ran up. "What is it? Is it good to eat? Shall we peck it?"

"No, no, no! You'll burst me if you do!" cried the balloon. "Leave me alone!"

One of the hens gave the balloon a sharp peck. But it wasn't quite sharp enough and the balloon didn't burst, though it didn't like the peck at all. The

other hen ran at it – but the balloon just bobbed over a fence in time. Oh dear, what a life!

It bobbed into a field where a hungry goat stood. Aha! What was this, thought the goat, and trotted up to the balloon. Something to eat? Something big and round that would make a very nice meal?

The goat put his hoof on the balloon, just by the string round its neck. He bent his head down to eat it – but the wind gave a puff, and off went the balloon once more, shivering in fright. "Alice, Alice, where are you? Come and fetch me!" cried the poor balloon.

The goat hadn't burst it – but he had loosened the string at the bottom. Little by little the air began to escape out of the neck of the balloon. It grew smaller.

The wind took it along again, and, will you believe it, it blew the balloon right over the hedge into Alice's own garden! What a remarkable thing!

Alice was there and saw the balloon

at once. "Oh!" she cried, running to it. "What a tiny little balloon! I never saw such a teeny-weeny one in my life! You're a baby one!"

Well! The balloon was most astonished. It didn't know it had gone small and was getting even smaller.

But it suddenly saw that Alice's hands seemed very, very big – so it knew it was now very small. It wasn't a giant any more.

Alice took it indoors and put the balloon with her brother's and sister's balloons.

How tiny it was! The others laughed at it.

"Call yourself a balloon! You're a tiddler! Wherever did you come from?"

"I was once a giant balloon," said the balloon, humbly. "I thought I would fly up to the moon and see if I was as big as he is. But I've gone small."

"You're going smaller," said the pink balloon. "You'll soon be gone to nothing. Poor thing!"

He was right.

The balloon shrank until it was nothing but a tiny bit of blue rubber. It felt very small and humble and good-for-nothing.

"Oh! If only I were big as I was before, I wouldn't boast, or grumble at my string and want to fly to the moon!" thought the tiny bit of rubber. "I'd be sensible. But I've lost my chance. I'm no good to anyone now."

But next day Alice's father took the balloon, undid the string, and blew and blew and blew into it.

It swelled up – it got big and round and fat. It had a broad, smiling face. It was ENORMOUS!

"Why! It's the balloon I got at the party! It must be!" cried Alice. "I know its face – and it's just as big! Don't you slip your string again and fly away, balloon – you may never come back again. You may even BURST!"

"Don't worry. I'm sensible now," said the big balloon, bobbing on the string. "I don't want to fly to the moon. I just want to be kept on a string and be happy with what I've got."

Alice has still got it. She has blown it up five times altogether, but it's still there – and it's very, very old for a balloon, because she has had it for just over two years.

I've seen it – and I've flown it on its string.

And I do like its face. It smiles, and smiles, and smiles!

The Tom Thumb fairies

Once upon a time there were some very small creatures called Tom Thumb fairies – so small that you could easily hold a hundred in the palm of your hand and hardly feel any weight.

They lived in some little red toadstools in Toadstool Village on the borders of Fairyland. The toadstools were small enough, goodness knows, but the fairies were so tiny that each toadstool was as big as a house to them. So they hung curtains at the windows in the top, and had a little door in the stalk with a knocker and a letter-box, just as you have.

Now one night there came a band of red goblins creeping round Toadstool

Village. It was a dark night and there were so many clouds that not even the stars gave their faint light. The goblin chief gave a signal, and at once two goblins went to each toadstool house, opened the door and captured the small fairy inside the bedroom at the top of the toadstool.

Nobody heard them squeal. Nobody heard them struggle. They were popped into bags and taken off to Goblin Town at once, there to wait on the goblins and help them with their spells. Their wings were clipped off, so that they could not fly home. The wings grew again in a few weeks' time, but every time they grew the goblins clipped them off again.

The Tom Thumb fairies were very unhappy. "What shall we do?" they wept. "We hate working underground all day long. We hate these red goblins, who are so unkind. We don't know the way home. We have no wings to fly with."

One day one of the Tom Thumb

fairies found a worm-hole leading up to the sunlight. She was overjoyed, and she whispered the news to the others.

"One morning when the goblins have gone off somewhere, we will creep up this worm-hole and escape," said the fairy.

"But the goblins will come after us," said the others. "We shan't know which way to go when we get up into daylight again."

"Never mind," said the first one. "We will see what we can do."

So the next time the red goblins went off together, leaving the Tom Thumb fairies to do all the work, the tiny creatures began to make their way up the worm-hole. It was very small – but they were smaller still.

Soon they came to the worm, and they could not get by, for the worm was fat and lay squeezed up in its bedroom – a large part of the hole halfway down the passage.

"Please move up a bit," said one of the

Tom Thumbs, poking the worm. "We want to get by."

The worm moved up its hole. It put out its head and listened, for it had no eyes to see with. Was any sharp-eyed bird about? No – it could hear no pattering of feet. So it drew itself right up and let the fairies use its rather slimy hole as a passage up to the daylight.

How pleased the Tom Thumbs were when they saw the bright sunshine again! "Now we must plan what to do," they cried.

"Get back into your hole," shouted a fairy to the worm. "The red goblins may come after us. Don't you move out of your hole for them, or they will catch us."

"There are plenty of other holes for the red goblins to come up by," said the worm, sliding back again. "There's the mouse-hole just over there – and the big rabbit-hole in the hedge – and any amount of empty worm-holes too."

"Oh dear!" said the Tom Thumbs, looking round as if they expected to see the red goblins at any moment. "We had better find a hiding-place in case they come. Where can we go?"

There were pink-tipped daisies about – much, much bigger than the Tom Thumb fairies. There was a large dandelion plant too, with great golden blossoms.

"I will hide you," said the dandelion in a soft silky voice. "You are so tiny that you can each slip under one of my many golden petals. Hurry now, for I can hear the red goblins coming."

In a trice the Tom Thumbs had run to the large dandelion, which spread its hundreds of soft petals to the sun. Each fairy lifted up a silken petal and slipped underneath. There they hid in safety whilst the red goblins, suddenly appearing from the mouse-hole, began to hunt for the Tom Thumbs.

"They must be somewhere about,"

shouted the chief one. "Hunt well, all of you."

Well, they hunted and they hunted, but no one thought of looking in the dandelion-head. There the Tom Thumbs hid, and did not make a movement for fear of being found.

"Well, goblins, we must get back to our home underground," said the chief at last. "But you, Gobo, and you, Feefo, and you, Huggo, stay up here and keep watch, in case those Tom Thumbs are hiding anywhere."

The goblins went back down the mouse-hole, but Gobo, Feefo and Huggo stayed behind, their sharp black eyes looking round and about. The Tom Thumbs did not dare to move.

"Don't you worry," whispered the dandelion. "You have a soft bed – and if you look hard you will find honey to eat, and when the night comes you will have dew to drink. Keep still and rest, and you will be safe."

Day after day the Tom Thumbs lay

hidden in the golden dandelion, whilst the three goblins kept a strict watch. The dandelion grew on its stalk and lifted the Tom Thumbs higher – and then something odd happened.

It was time for the golden dandelion-head to fade. The gold left it – it closed up like a bud once more, holding the Tom Thumbs safely inside. It was no longer a wide golden flower, but a rather untidy-looking dead one, tightly shut. It drooped its head so low that it hid it amongst the leaves. Still the Tom Thumbs lay hidden – because now they could not get out!

What would happen to them? They did not know. The honey was almost finished, and the dew no longer fell on to them for drink. They huddled together in the dead flower, frightened and miserable.

The stalk of the dandelion grew longer and longer. How strange! But it had a reason. Yes – for the flower was turning into seed – and when that seed was ready it must be taken up into the air on a long, long stalk so that the wind might blow it away. Oh, clever dandelion!

So it came about that one day the dead dandelion raised its head again, on its long, long stalk. It stood straight up once more, and – wonder of wonders! – instead of a golden head it now had a head full of marvellous white seeds. It was a beautiful dandelion clock.

And now the Tom Thumb fairies began to get excited. "Look!" they cried. "The dandelion has grown us little parachutes! Do look! There is one for each of us. We can hold on to the stalk – it is like a handle for us – and when the wind blows, the parachute of hairs will carry us far, far away from here, safe from the red goblins."

But the wind did not blow them away – someone else did. Who was that? Well, it may have been you! A little girl came down that way and saw the dandelion clock standing there, so tall and beautiful. She did not see the three red goblins still keeping a sharp watch. She picked the dandelion clock and looked at it.

"I shall blow you," she said. "I want to know the time. Now then – PUFF! – one o'clock. PUFF! – two o'clock. PUFF! – three o'clock. PUFF! – four o'clock. PUFF! – five o'clock. Oh, it's tea-time! I must hurry."

She ran off, pleased to see the pretty seeds blowing in the air – but she didn't see that each one carried a Tom Thumb fairy.

The dandelion seeds flew high and far. When at last they came to the ground they were far, far away from the red goblins' home. The Tom Thumbs took the first bus home they could find; and now they are safe in Toadstool Village again – and at night they all lock and bolt their doors!

Wasn't it lucky for them that they hid in a dandelion?

The Banana Man

All the toys were very excited, because there was going to be a fancy dress party at midnight. There was to be a prize for the best dress of all, and another prize for the funniest.

"I'm going to dress up as the Fairy Queen," said the big doll.

"That's easy for you," said the baby doll. "You've only got to make yourself a crown and a pair of wings, because you have a dress fit for a queen already!"

"I'll make you a pair of fluffy ears and pin a tail on behind you and you can go as a rabbit, baby doll," said the teddy.

"Oh, thank you," said the doll. "That's kind of you. What will *you* go as, Teddy?"

"Something funny, I think," said the bear. "I can't win a prize for the best dress, but I might for the funniest."

"Tell me what you're going to be!" begged the pink cat. "I'll help you."

"Well, I don't know yet," said the bear. "So don't bother me. What are *you* going as, pink cat?"

"An elephant," said the pink cat.

"Don't be silly," said the baby doll. "You can't possibly go as an elephant."

"Well, I thought I could walk backwards and wave my tail so that everyone would think I was walking towards them waving my trunk," said the pink cat.

"You sound quite mad," said the bear. "You won't look like an elephant waving a trunk, you'll simply look like a rather silly cat walking backwards."

"Oh, don't quarrel," said the baby doll. "You go into a corner and think about what you're going to be, Teddy."

So the bear went and leaned against the waste-paper basket and tried to think of something. But he couldn't. Whatever could he dress up in? He really must choose something funny.

He smelt a sweetish smell. It came from the inside of the waste-paper basket. Teddy got up and looked inside. One of the children had eaten a banana and thrown the yellow skin there.

The teddy bear stared at it – and a great thought came into his head. Couldn't he get into that banana skin, ask the baby doll to sew the sides up for him, and make holes for his arms and legs – and his head would stick out of the top. He would be a Banana Man. Nobody had ever been a Banana Man before. It was a really wonderful idea!

He fetched the banana skin and went over to the baby doll. He told her about his idea and she giggled.

"Oh, dear! How everyone will laugh! It's the funniest dress I ever heard of. Now, let me make two holes at the bottom of the skin for your legs – there – I'll make the arm-holes later on when you're in the skin with your legs through their holes."

They went into a dark corner of the toy cupboard to finish the banana dress, and everyone wondered what the giggling in the corner was about.

But when it came to sewing up the skin, the baby doll couldn't do it. The cotton slipped in and out of the banana skin and the sides wouldn't hold together.

"It's no good," said the doll, in despair. "We'll have to get the elf in to do it for you. She's marvellous with her needle. I'll go and call her."

So she called the elf in, the one who had a cosy little home in the ivy outside the window. The elf took one look at Teddy in the banana skin and said, "Zips!"

"Pardon?" said the baby doll.

"Zips," said the elf. "That's what you need to keep these skins tightly done up. I'll go and get my zips, and put them in for you."

She ran off and soon came back with some zip-fastenings, which she put in the banana skins with a bit of magic. Then she zipped up the banana with the teddy bear inside!

The baby doll began to laugh. "Oh, dear – you do look so funny, Teddy! Your body is the banana, and your arms and legs and head are sticking out of it. You really look like a walking banana!"

The bear began to do a solemn dance, waving his arms and kicking up his legs. The elf and the baby doll laughed till they cried.

"You'll certainly win the prize for the funniest dress!" they said.

And he did. Nobody could help roaring with laughter at him. The pink cat was quite alarmed when he first saw him, because he had really no idea it was Teddy. He thought it was a live banana with arms and legs and a head!

The big doll got the prize for the most beautiful dress. The bear was very proud indeed when he had to go up and get the prize for the funniest. He capered all the way and the pink cat had to sit down because he was laughing so much that he kept falling over.

"So glad you got the prize, Teddy," said the elf. "I must run now, because I'm off to catch the night-bat to go and stay with my aunt. See you in two weeks' time. Goodbye!"

Off she went. Then the toys began to take off their fancy dresses and put them away. But dear me, the bear couldn't unzip his banana skin. It just wouldn't come undone.

The baby doll tried. The big doll tried, and the pink cat tried. But not one of them could unzip that banana.

"You know, the elf put the zips in with a touch of magic," said the big doll at last. "And *I* think it needs a touch of magic to get them undone again."

"The elf's gone away for two weeks," said the baby doll, remembering. "Oh, Teddy – you'll have to be a Banana Man for two whole weeks!"

"Whatever will the children say when they find me dressed up in a banana skin?" said the bear, in a small voice. "They won't know me. They won't like me, either. And certainly they won't take me to bed with them. Nobody would take a Banana Man to bed. Oh, dear – this is a very sad thing."

He was so upset about it that he sat down on his prize without knowing it; and as it was a lovely cream cake it didn't look much of a prize when the bear got up again.

"Lick it off me," said the bear, gloomily, to the pink cat. So the pink cat did, and really enjoyed it.

"Banana cream," said the pink cat. "Very nice indeed!"

Well, all this happened last week, and the bear is still a Banana Man, because the elf hasn't come back. And tomorrow the children mean to take him out to tea with them – so what they will say when they find him in the banana skin I really can't imagine. What would *you* say?

A coat for the snowman

Old Mrs White looked out of her bedroom window and frowned. "Snow!" she said. "Snow – thick and white and deep! How annoying. What a lot must have fallen in the night."

"Oh, look at the lovely snow!" shouted the children in the field nearby. "It's as high as our knees. Let's build a snowman."

"Silly children to play with the cold snow like that," said Mrs White, who wasn't very fond of children. "Now I suppose they will play in the field all day and make a terrible noise. Bother them all."

Micky, Katie, Olive, Peter and Will played together in the snowy field that

day and had a lovely time. They made their snowman. He was a real beauty.

He had a big round head, with twigs sticking out for hair. He had eyes of stones and a big white stone for a nose. He had a stone for a mouth, too.

He had a big fat body, and the children patted it all round to make it smooth. He looked very real.

"We must dress him," said Micky. "We want a hat for him." He found an old hat in a ditch. It just fitted the snowman nicely. He wore it a little to one side and looked very knowing indeed.

"We want a scarf, too," said Katie. "My aunt lives in that cottage nearby. I'll see if she has one."

She had. It was an old red one, rather holey, but it went round the snowman's neck quite well.

"He'll feel warm with this scarf," said Olive. "It must be so cold to be made of snow. I do wish we had a coat for him to wear."

"Ooooh yes – then we could fill the sleeves with snow, and that would make him look awfully real," said Katie. "I'll ask my aunt for an old coat."

But her aunt said no, she hadn't a coat old enough for a snowman.

"Where can we get one?" asked Katie. "Shall I ask the old lady next door to you? What's her name? Mrs White?"

"Oh, you won't get anything out of *her*," said her aunt. "She doesn't like children. She's a grumbly old thing. You leave her alone."

"She looks very poor," said Olive. "Hasn't she got much money?"

"Hardly any," said Katie's aunt. "Don't you go bothering her, now – she'll box your ears if you do."

The children went back to their snowman. They looked at him. It would be so very, very nice if he had a coat. He would be the finest snowman in the world then.

Just then old Mrs White, in big rubber boots, came grumbling out to get herself a scuttleful of coal. Micky saw her.

"Poor old thing," he said. "I'll get the coal for her." He hopped over the fence and went down the snowy garden. Old Mrs White saw him and frowned.

"Now, what are you doing coming into my garden without asking?" she scolded.

"I'll get your coal in for you," said Micky. "Give me that shovel."

He shovelled until the scuttle was full. Then he carried it indoors for Mrs White.

"That's kind of you," she said. "But I hope you're not expecting money for that. I've none to spare."

"Oh no, of course not," said Micky, quite shocked. "My mother won't let me take money for doing bits of kindness. She says they're not kindnesses if you're paid for them. I don't want any reward at all, thank you, Mrs White."

"Well now, I wish I could give you something, that I do," said Mrs White, feeling pleased with the little boy. "But I've no biscuits and no sweets. You just look around my kitchen and tell me if there's anything you'd like now. What about that little china dog?"

"I don't want anything, thank you," said Micky, looking round. He suddenly saw an old, old coat hanging up behind the scullery door.

"Well," he said, "there's just one thing – do you think you could possibly lend us that old coat for our snowman, Mrs White? Only just *lend* it to us. We'll bring it back safely."

"Why, yes, if you want it," said old Mrs White. "It's a dirty, ragged old thing. I haven't worn it for years. I keep meaning to give it away. Yes, you take it. I shan't even want it back."

"Oh, thank you," said Micky. "Our snowman *will* look grand."

He unhooked the old coat from the door and ran back to the others with it. "Look what I've got!" he called. "Mrs White's given it to me for our snowman. Won't he look grand?"

The children filled the sleeves with snow and then hung the coat round the snowman. He certainly did look real now. There he stood in his old hat, scarf and coat, looking very fine.

"How do you do, Mr Shivers?" said Micky, walking up to the snowman and holding out his hand. "I hope you like this cold weather."

The others roared with laughter. The people passing by looked over the hedge at the snowman and called out that he was the best one they had seen. The children really felt very proud of him.

They left him standing there alone when it grew dark. But the next day they were back again. Alas, the snow had begun to melt, and Mr Shivers was a peculiar sight. He had slumped down, and all the snow had trickled out of his sleeves.

"He's going," said Micky. "I'll take my aunt's old scarf back to her."

"We don't need to take Mrs White's

coat back. She said we could keep it," said Peter. "Still, perhaps we'd better."

Micky jerked the coat off the melting snowman. He ripped the lining a little, and a piece of paper fell out.

"I say, what's this?" said Micky in surprise. "Why, it's paper money. It's a ten-pound note. It must have slipped out of the pocket into the lining, and old Mrs White didn't know it was there. Gracious, let's go and show it to her."

They all tore off to Mrs White's cottage. She could hardly believe her eyes when she saw the paper money. "Why, now, I lost that ten-pound note years and years ago," she said. "And proper upset I was about it, too. Thought I'd dropped it in the street, and all the time it was in my coat-lining. What a bit of good luck for me."

"Yes," said Katie. "I'm so glad."

"Bless your heart! What nice children you are. Maybe I've been wrong about boys and girls," said old Mrs White. "Well, well, now I can buy myself a new shawl and a new pair of shoes for my poor old feet."

She bought something else, too. She bought the biggest chocolate cake she could buy; she bought a pound of mixed biscuits, a pound of mixed chocolates, five big balloons and a big box of crackers. And she gave a party for Micky, Katie, Olive, Peter and Will.

They loved it. But in the middle of it Micky gave her quite a shock. "There's somebody who ought to have come to this party and isn't here," he said solemnly. "*What* a pity."

"Oh dear me, who's that?" said Mrs White, quite alarmed. "I *am* sorry I've forgotten one of you. Go and fetch him at once."

"We can't," said Micky, and he laughed. "It's Mr Shivers, the snowman, Mrs White. He ought to be the guest of honour, for without him we'd never have borrowed your coat and we wouldn't have found the money. What a pity old Mr Shivers isn't here."

Off with their shadows!

"I hope those naughty little pixies don't come tonight," said the sailor doll. "They would spoil our nice party."

"They really are very mischievous," said the pink rabbit. "They upset the poor clockwork mouse very much by pretending they had thrown his key out of the window – and all the time it was in the brick-box."

"Yes – and they shouldn't have locked the dolls' house front door so that the little dolls couldn't get out," said the bear. "And they shouldn't have wound up the little car and set it running round the playroom all by itself, so that it knocked down half the Noah's Ark animals who were out walking!"

"Well, if they come tonight we will *not* let them join our party," said the sailor doll.

The party began. It was a bright moonlit night and the toys could see everything beautifully, because the moon looked in at the window all the time.

There was plenty to eat. The dolls' house dolls had been busy cooking all the evening on the little stove in their kitchen. The musical box played for dancing, and everything was very merry and bright.

And then those mischievous pixies arrived as usual! They flew in at the crack of the window and stood looking in delight at the party. "Hurrah! A party! Now we can join in and have a good time, too!"

"You can't come to a party if you're not invited," said the clockwork clown, and gave the nearest pixie a push.

"Oh, he pushed me, he pushed me!" cried the pixie. "Off with his shadow!"

The toys saw that the chief pixie had a little pair of scissors with her, and they were surprised.

"What do you mean – 'Off with his shadow'?" asked the curly-haired doll.

"Just what we say! Off with his shadow!" cried the pixies. "We're collecting shadows. We can sell them, you know. They make invisible cloaks. When anyone puts on a cloak made from shadows, he can't be seen! He becomes invisible at once."

"Good gracious! You don't *really* mean to say you're collecting shadows for that?" cried the pink rabbit. "How dare you?"

"Well, let us come to your party, then," said the pixies.

"No. We don't like you and we don't want you," said the teddy bear, quite fiercely. "You're just mischievous nuisances."

"Go away!" shouted the rest of the toys.

"Off with their shadows!" cried the

pixies in glee, and then, dear me, what a snip-snip-snipping there was!

The bear heard the scissors snipping behind him, and he turned in alarm. His nice fat little shadow was being snipped away where it stretched behind him. What a shame! The pixie rolled it up and threw it to another, who stuffed it into a bag.

Then the scissors went snipping behind the rabbit, and although he tried to run away, he couldn't until his shadow had been snipped from his feet and rolled up like the first one.

"Who's next, who's next?" cried the pixies. "Off with their shadows! They won't let us come to their party!"

Off went the curly-haired doll's big shadow and the clockwork mouse's tiny one. Off went the sailor doll's. What an upset there was, as the little black shadows were snipped away and thrown into the bag.

"Come into the dark corners!" cried the clockwork clown. "We don't have shadows in the dark, dark corners. Quick, join me over here!"

So all the rest of the toys ran to the dark corners, where their shadows

couldn't be seen. The pixies laughed.

"We've got enough shadows to make a simply wonderful cloak to sell to Mr High-Hat the wizard," they shouted. "Goodbye! It serves you right for not letting us come to your party!"

Well, what a to-do there was when those mischievous pixies had flown out of the window! The toys who had had their shadows snipped off stood in the moonlight crying because they hadn't any shadows stretching out behind them.

"It isn't as if our shadows were ever much *good* to us," sobbed the little mouse. "But it's dreadful not to have them. I don't feel right without a shadow running about with me."

"I think we'd better go and complain to the old owl in the tree outside the window," said the pink rabbit. "He's very, very wise. Everyone knows that. He might know where the pixies have gone and go after them to get our shadows back for us."

So they called out through the crack in the window. "Hoo-hoo-hoo, the owl, are you there? We want your advice, please."

Hoo-hoo-hoo flew to the window-sill. The toys told him all about the mischievous pixies and how they had shouted "Off with their shadows!" and snipped them away to make a cloak.

"Ha! They tried to do that to me, too, when they thought I was sleeping on a bough – but I wasn't," said the owl. "They all fell off the branch in a hurry when I opened my eyes and hooted. Don't worry. I'll go after them and fetch your shadows back. Have a needle and black cotton ready to sew them on, because they will go out of shape if they are away from you for very long."

The toys got ready some needles threaded with black cotton, and waited anxiously for the owl to come back.

He came at last and sat on the window-sill. "Hoo-hoo, too-whit!" he said. "I'm back. But, toys, I'm sorry to say that those naughty little pixies have already sewn your shadows into a big cloak."

"Oh, dear!" said the toys in dismay. "What are we to do, then?"

The owl began to laugh. "Ho-ho-ho, hoo-hoo-hoo! I told those pixies I would pick them up in my big talons and drop them in the very middle of the pond if they didn't give me some shadows to take back to you!" he said.

"And did they?" cried the toys.

"Yes! They were so scared that they cut each other's shadows off, rolled them up and gave them to me," said the owl, and he showed them something he was holding in his left foot. "Here they are, all ready for you."

"Oh, thank you, thank you, thank you!" said the toys, in delight, and they caught the little soft bundle of shadows that the owl pushed through the window crack.

"Quick – we must sew them on before

they lose their shape," said the sailor doll – and you should have seen how busy they all were, sewing on those shadows to the heels of the toys that had lost them.

At last they were all on. "Oh, good!" said the clockwork mouse. "It's nice to have a shadow again. Let's go and stand in the bright moonlight and see if they are exactly like our own shadows."

So they went to stand in the moonlight – and the rabbit gave a shout. "I say! Look at *my* shadow! It's got wings!"

"So has *my* shadow – and pointed ears like pixies have!" cried the teddy bear. "*I* haven't got ears like that. Oh, dear – my shadow does look strange!"

"It's the shadow of a *pixie*," said the curly-haired doll. "Mine's like that, too. Look – it's got pointed ears, a little head – and wings! It's nice to have a shadow with wings. I've always wanted wings, and I shall feel as if I've got them when I look at my winged shadow!"

Wasn't it strange – each toy that had lost his own shadow had a pixie shadow now! What could they do about it? Nothing at all! Their own shadows were made up into a magic cloak and given to the wizard. They had to put up with pixie shadows instead.

They really felt rather grand, and the toys whose shadows hadn't been cut off felt quite jealous. They would have liked pixies' shadows, too!

But *what* do you suppose the children will say when they next play with their toys? They will stand up the sailor doll – and see that his shadow belongs to a pixie! The rabbit will show a pixie shadow, too, and so will the little clockwork mouse! What a thrill for the children! They won't know what to make of it, will they?

I do hope they will read this story, and then they will know exactly what has happened. If they do, I shall expect them to write to me and ask me to come and see the toys with the pixie shadows.

The swallow fairy

Once there was a small fairy who played all summer long with the swallows. She had long curved wings as they had, and she flashed in the air with them, racing them over the fields and back.

They lived on the insects they caught in the air. The swallow fairy lived on the nectar she found in the flowers. The bees and butterflies showed her how to get it with a long, very tiny spoon.

"We have a tongue to put into the flowers, to suck out the nectar," they said, "but you haven't a long enough one. So use a spoon."

Now, in October, a cold wind blew. The swallow fairy shivered. There were not so many flowers with honey in and she was sometimes hungry.

There were not so many insects flying in the air either, so the swallows were often hungry. And when the cold wind blew, they gathered together on the roofs of barns and on the telegraph wires, chattering and twittering.

The little martins were there with the swallows, too. They were cousins of the swallows, and loved to fly with them high in the sky. "Don't let's stay here in this cold wind!" they cried. "Let's fly off to a warmer country."

"Yes, do let's!" said the swallows. "In a warmer country there will be more insects. There are so few here now. We will go!"

"Oh, don't leave me!" cried the swallow fairy. "I shall be so lonely. Take me with you."

"It's too far for you to fly," said her best friend, a fine long-tailed swallow with a shining steel-blue back. "You would fall into the sea and be drowned."

"Oh, will you fly across the sea?" said the fairy. "I shouldn't like that. I'll stay here – but you will come back again?"

"In the springtime," said the swallow, and then suddenly, almost as if one of them had given a signal, the whole twittering flock flew into the air and wheeled away to the south. They were gone. Not one was left.

The fairy was lonely. She sat crying in the evening wind, sitting on a barn roof by herself. A little black bat saw her and flew near.

"Come and live with me!" he cried. "Do come!"

So the fairy went to live with him. But as the wind grew colder he wouldn't go out to fly. He hung himself upside down in an old cave, with hundreds of others like himself. And he went to sleep!

"Wake up, wake up!" cried the fairy. "You're a dull sort of friend to have, little bat!"

"Leave me alone," said the bat, sleepily. "I'm too cold to fly. I shall sleep till the sun comes again in the spring. Hang yourself upside down, fairy, and sleep, too."

"I don't like hanging upside down," said the fairy. "I don't like hanging myself up at all. And I don't like this cave, either. It smells."

"Well, go and live with someone else then," said the bat, in a huff, and he wouldn't say another word.

The fairy flew off. She came to a pond and sat by it, feeling cold and lonely. A frog was there, talking to a fat, squat toad.

"Hallo, fairy!" said the frog. "Why do you look so miserable?"

"I'm lonely," said the fairy. "I've no friend to live with."

"You'd better tuck yourself away somewhere for the winter," said the frog. "Come with me and I'll keep you close to me, little fairy."

"All right," said the fairy. "Where are you going?"

"I'm going down into the mud at the

bottom of the pond," said the frog. "I shall sleep there all the winter. It's a nice cosy place to sleep."

"Oh, I'd *hate* that!" said the fairy and shivered. "Cold and muddy and wet! I'd rather go with the toad. I always did like his lovely brown eyes."

"Yes, you come with me," said the toad, and took her to a big stone. Underneath was a fine hiding-place, just big enough for the fairy and himself. He dragged her underneath with him. Then he shut his eyes. The fairy went to sleep, too. But she soon awoke and shivered.

"This is a nasty damp place," she said. "I shall get a cold. Toad, let's go somewhere else?"

But the toad was fast asleep and wouldn't answer. So the fairy left him in disgust. She walked fast to keep herself warm – and ran into a hedgehog, also hurrying fast. He carried a leaf in his mouth.

"Oh, hullo!" said the fairy. "Where are

you off to, with that leaf?"

"I've got a cosy little house in a warm bank," said the hedgehog. "I'm lining it with leaves. Why don't you come and live with me there? It's really a very nice little home, with a curtain of moss for a door."

"All right, I'll come," said the fairy, who thought the hedgehog's home sounded nice. It *was* nice, too, all lined with dry dead leaves, and quite warm.

But the hedgehog was so prickly that the fairy couldn't possibly cuddle up to him. And whenever he moved, his prickles stuck into her. That wasn't at all nice.

"I'll have to go," said the fairy. "I'm sorry, but you're not very cuddly, hedgehog."

The hedgehog said nothing. He was fast asleep. He wouldn't wake up for weeks!

"This is very boring," said the fairy to herself, scrambling out of the warm hole. "All my friends seem either to be flying off to warmer lands, or finding places to sleep away the winter. I don't want to do either, but I *must* find somewhere for a home. And I'd dearly like to have a nice friend I could talk to, too, not one who's going to snore all winter long."

She met a snake, and he invited her to go to a hollow tree he knew and curl up with him and all his friends together. "We knot ourselves together for warmth." he said. "It's an awfully nice tree we go to, fairy. Do come."

"Well – no, thank you," said the fairy. "I like snakes and I think they're very clever the way they glide along without feet – but I don't want to be knotted up with you all winter. I might want to get out and not be able to, because I'm sure you'd all be fast asleep."

"Oh, we should," said the snake. "Well, what about trying the dormouse? He's a nice cosy fellow, and he would keep you warm and not mind a bit if you wriggled in and out of his hole during the winter. He's in the ditch over there."

The dormouse was very fat. He told the fairy that as he never had anything to eat all the winter, he liked to get as nice and fat as possible before he went to sleep.

"Don't you ever wake up in the winter?" said the fairy. "I really do want a cosy, furry friend like you to cuddle up to, but it's so dull having a friend who is asleep all the time and never says a word. And oh dear! I don't know *what* I shall do for food soon. There isn't any nectar to be found at all, except in a few odd flowers here and there."

The dormouse went close to her and whispered, "I know where there is a store of nuts. Do you like nuts?"

"Oh, yes," said the fairy. "Very much."

"Well, do you see that clump of ivy over there?" asked the dormouse, pointing with his tiny foot. "I happen to know there are about a dozen nuts there. You could feast on those."

"Oh, thank you," said the fairy. She watched the dormouse go down to his little hole in some tree-roots. She liked him very much – but he *would* be dull as a friend, because she knew what a sleepy fellow he was.

She flew to the ivy and found the nuts. She was just wondering how to crack one when she heard a cross voice: "Hey! Don't take my nuts!"

"Oh – are they yours? I'm so sorry," said the fairy, and put the nut back quickly. She looked at the animal beside her. She liked him very much. He was a red squirrel, with bright eyes and a very bushy tail.

The squirrel looked at the fairy, and he liked her, too. He was suddenly sorry he had been cross, because the fairy looked cold and hungry and lonely. He took up a nut. "Would you like me to give you one?" he said. "I don't like people to steal them, but I never mind giving them away."

He gnawed through the shell, and got out the nut. He gave it to the fairy. "Oh, thank you," she said, and began to nibble it.

"You seem very hungry," said the squirrel. "Where is your home?"

"I haven't one," said the fairy, and she told him how she had tried to find someone to live with in warmth and friendliness. "You see – so many creatures go to sleep all the winter – and that's dull, isn't it?"

"Very dull," agreed the squirrel. "I think what *I* do is much more sensible. I sleep in my cosy hole when the weather is very bitter, with my tail wrapped round me for a rug – and when a warm spell comes, I wake up, scamper down my tree and find my nuts to have a feast. I have a good play, and then when the frosty night comes again, I pop back to sleep."

"That does sound a good idea," said the fairy. "Sleep the coldest days away – wake up in the sunshine and play, and have a good meal – and go back again when the frost nips your toes. You're the most sensible of all the creatures I know, Squirrel. How I wish you were my friend!"

"I'd like to be," said the squirrel. "You come with me to my hole and sleep with me, wrapped up in my tail. And perhaps, in the springtime, when I want to go and find a nice little wife, you'd brush and comb my fur well, and make me beautiful."

"Oh, I *will*!" said the fairy. "I'd love to do that."

So up the tree they went, and the squirrel curled up in his hole with the fairy beside him. He wrapped his bushy tail round them both, and they slept cosily together.

And when a warm spell comes they both wake up and look for the squirrel's nuts. So, if ever you see a red squirrel scampering in the winter sunshine, look around and see if you can spy his small companion hiding anywhere.

The fair at Oak Tree Town

"I say, Flip," cried Binkle, rushing into Heather Cottage in very great excitement. "What do you think is coming to Oak Tree Town?"

"What?" asked Flip.

"A fair!" said Binkle – "a fair with roundabouts and swings and just everything! Won't it be fun!"

"Yes, but we haven't got any money to go on the roundabouts," said Flip dolefully.

"No, that's a pity," frowned Binkle, and pulled at his whiskers and rubbed his nose. Suddenly he stopped and his eyes opened wide.

"Flip!" he said. "Flip!"

"What?" asked Flip.

"Oh, Flip!" said Binkle again, in a voice of deepest excitement. "Flip!"

"Stop Flipping me," said Flip, "and tell me what you want to say."

"Flip," said Binkle, "I've got the most *wonderful* idea I've ever had!"

"Then I'd rather you kept it to yourself," said Flip, hurriedly folding up his newspaper. "You oughtn't to *let* yourself have ideas, Binkle."

"Flip, listen!" cried Binkle, catching hold of him and sitting him down plump! in his chair again. "Wouldn't you like to have enough money to go on *all* the roundabouts and *all* the swings and see *all* the side-shows?"

"Rather!" said Flip.

"Well, I'll tell you how we can," began Binkle. "You know how folk love to throw balls at things, in a fair, don't you? They *love* throwing at coconuts and things like that."

"Yes," said Flip.

"Well, Flip," said Binkle, "wouldn't it be lovely if we could somehow have

Herbert Hedgehog to throw at? Think how exciting it would be to see if you could throw a ball and get it stuck on one of his prickles!"

"Binkle," said Flip in horror, "whatever will you think of next! As if Herbert would ever agree to that, anyhow!"

"No, he wouldn't *agree*," said Binkle thoughtfully, "but I might be able to think of some way that didn't need his consent."

Well, after a few days, Binkle *did* think of a way, but he was so afraid Flip would refuse to help him that he decided not to tell everything.

"Look here, Flip," he said, "I just want you to take a letter to Herbert for me, will you?"

"All right," said Flip, reaching for his cap. "Let me read the letter first, Binkle."

Binkle read it out loud: "Dear Herbert Hedgehog, as you are one of the most important people of Oak Tree Town, we should be very much obliged if you would come and open our fair for us tomorrow at three o'clock sharp!"

"But I don't see the sense of writing a letter like that!" said Flip in astonishment.

"You wait and see!" grinned Binkle. "That will be sure to bring Herbert to the fair all dressed up in his best, and with his new gold watch and all!"

"Still, I don't see how we –" began Flip, but Binkle sent him scurrying off, telling him to be sure no one saw him putting the letter into Herbert's letter-box.

Well, when Herbert got that letter, wasn't he pleased and proud!

"Oho!" he said to himself, standing all his prickles on end. "So the fair people want me to open their show for them, do they? What will all Oak Tree Town say to *that*? I must dress up in my very best!"

He did. And very grand he looked. Last of all he put on his lovely new gold watch and chain. Then he looked at himself in the glass and was very pleased indeed with his appearance.

He set off for the fair, wishing that he could meet Sammy Squirrel or Dilly Duck, so that he might see their faces when he told them he was to open the fair.

But all he met were Flip and Binkle Bunny, also on their way to the fair.

"My!" said Binkle, when he caught sight of Herbert. "My, Herbert! I never saw you so grand before. How fine you look!"

"I'm going to open the fair," said Herbert importantly, swelling himself out proudly.

"Well, well, well!" said Binkle, holding up his paws, pretending to be most astonished. "They made a good choice when they asked you, Herbert. I don't know anybody who could do it better."

Herbert felt very pleased. He began to think Binkle wasn't such a bad fellow after all.

"Come along with me and hear my

opening speech," he said.

"We'd love to," said Binkle. "Wouldn't we, Flip?"

"Yes," agreed Flip, who was very much wondering what would happen when Herbert discovered he wasn't going to open the fair after all!

"But you know, Herbert," said Binkle solemnly, "you shouldn't have dressed yourself up so grandly, and you *certainly* shouldn't have put on your gold watch."

"Why not?" asked Herbert in alarm.

"Well, there are always a rough lot of people at any fair," said Binkle gravely, "and if they see you dressed up like that, they might think you'd a lot of money on you – and rob you!"

"O–oh dear!" said Herbert nervously. "And I've got my new watch on, too. I wish I hadn't come. I think I'll go home."

"Oh no, don't do that," cried Binkle. "If you like, Herbert, Flip and I will stay with you and look after you."

"Oh, *thank* you!" cried Herbert,

thinking that Flip and Binkle were certainly two very nice fellows. "That will be fine. Well, here we are at the fair."

They went through the gates, and Herbert stared in astonishment.

"The fair's begun," he cried. "Surely I'm not late!"

"We must be," said Binkle. "Oh, what a pity, Herbert! Now you can't open the fair."

Herbert was terribly disappointed.

"I'm going to see the head man about it," he snorted. "He's no business to ask me to come, and then to open the fair without me."

But the head man was very rude. He laughed at Herbert, and said he was mad. Then he became angry and told Herbert to go away, or he'd put him into a coconut shy.

Binkle and Flip pulled him away.

"Never mind," said Binkle. "And don't say any more, for goodness sake, Herbert. Else you really *will* be put into a coconut shy. These people can be very rough, you know. And, oh dear, it is a pity you came all dressed up like this! I'm so afraid you'll be robbed."

Herbert clung to Binkle and begged him not to leave him.

"No, I won't," promised Binkle. "Come and look round, Herbert."

He took Herbert by the arm and led him off. Then Binkle did a very strange thing. He frowned and looked crossly at every single person he met. And, of course, *they* frowned back.

Presently Herbert noticed how crossly everyone looked at them.

"Why does everybody frown at us?" he asked in surprise.

"I'm afraid they don't like you," said Binkle. "I expect the head man has said that you are not a nice person."

Herbert began to shiver with fright. Just then three badgers and two stoats passed by and frowned most fiercely. He shivered even more.

"Here, Flip," said Binkle suddenly,

"just look after Herbert for a minute. I'm going to talk to those fellows who've just passed us, and find out what's the matter with them!"

He left Herbert and Flip and ran up to the badgers and stoats.

"Hey, you fellows!" he said, "would you like to go in for a fine new throwing game?"

"What sort?" asked a badger.

"Well, you see old Herbert Hedgehog there," said Binkle. "I believe I can get him to sit down and let you throw potatoes at him to see if you can get them stuck on his prickles!"

The badgers grinned.

"Never heard of that before," said one. "How much does he charge?"

"I'll go and ask him," said Binkle, and ran back to Herbert.

"I asked them why they looked so angrily at us," he said to Herbert, "and what do you think they said?"

"What?" asked Herbert and Flip.

"They said they'd never seen such an

ugly fellow as you before, and the sight of your face was enough to make the fair a failure," said Binkle untruthfully. "I'm very much afraid you're in for a rough time, Herbert. You saw how everybody scowled at you, didn't you?"

Poor Herbert Hedgehog! He shivered and shook, and shook and shivered, and wished heartily that he'd never come to the fair at all.

"What shall I do?" he asked. "I'd better go home."

"I shouldn't do that," said Binkle; "it would look as if you were running away. No, I know a simpler plan than that."

"What?" asked Herbert eagerly.

"I'll take you to a quiet seat I know over there," said Binkle, pointing. "There's a wall just behind it, and you can sit facing it, pretending to read a newspaper. Then your back will be to the passers-by, and no one will know who you are."

"They won't bother about my face if they can't see it," said Herbert, with a sigh. "All right, I'll do as you say."

"Take him, Flip," ordered Binkle, his wicked eyes dancing with delight and his nose going up and down with excitement.

Flip took Herbert off, and sat him down on the seat Binkle had pointed out, facing a wall. He gave him a newspaper, and then turned to see whatever Binkle was doing.

He was talking excitedly to a small crowd of badgers, stoats and moles.

"Come on," he said. "You can have six throws. There he is, sitting over there, waiting for you to throw at him."

"Ha! ha!" chuckled Miner Mole, polishing his spectacles. "I'd like a good old throw at Herbert. He told me my cabbages were good for caterpillars but not for anything else, the other day."

"And he said my beetroots would pass very well as radishes," grinned a badger. "Come on, boys, let's have a shot at him! What luck!"

A small crowd moved towards

Herbert. Binkle produced a big basket full of potatoes which he had dug up from his garden that morning and hidden behind a tent, for he had no money to buy balls. From the basket he took a big notice, and balanced it upright against Herbert's seat.

Six throws a penny!
Spike a potato on
Herbert!

Then he started the game by throwing a few potatoes at Herbert.

Well, the pennies began to roll in like anything. Directly Flip saw what was happening, he began giggling, but Binkle stopped him.

"Be quiet, Flip!" he whispered fiercely. "You've got to keep Herbert still and pick up the potatoes. Pretend you're throwing them back! You can throw them to me and I'll put them in the basket."

Whizz! Whizz! Whizz!

149

The potatoes began spinning through the air, and Herbert gave a tremendous yell of fright and almost fell off his seat.

"It's all right! Keep still!" said Flip. "Your prickles will protect you, Herbert. I'll pick up the potatoes and throw them back, and keep the fellows off. Don't you worry!"

But Herbert *did* worry. He groaned, grunted, and yelled terrifically whenever a potato stuck on one of his prickles.

The crowd was delighted. Everyone thought Herbert was making a noise to amuse them, and more and more folk came up to join in the fun. The potatoes whizzed merrily through the air and stuck on Herbert, or burst into a score of pieces on the wall behind and spattered into poor Herbert's face. Flip picked up the whole ones and threw them back to Binkle as fast as he could.

"Don't you fret, Herbert," he panted. "I'm keeping them off all right."

Soon half the people of Oak Tree

Town came to join in the fun. Dilly Duck and Sammy Squirrel and Brock Badger joined in, and laughed till tears ran from their eyes, to hear Herbert grunting and groaning.

Then Binkle caught sight of Wily Weasel, Oak Tree Town's policeman. At first he was frightened – then an idea came to him.

"Hello, Wily!" he called. "Six a penny! Have a penn'orth?"

Now Wily was a very good shot. He took six potatoes, stood back, and threw them quickly one after the other at Herbert.

Every single one stuck on Herbert's prickles.

But that was too much for Herbert. With a fierce howl of rage he swung himself off the seat, and faced Wily, who had just bought another six and was preparing to throw.

Herbert stared in amazement at Wily.

"Wily!" he gasped. "Wily Weasel the Policeman! Why didn't you rescue me

instead of joining these fellows? And Dilly! and Brock! And Sammy! How can you all stand by and see me treated like this? *Gr-rrr-rrr!*"

He suddenly picked up a handful of potatoes and flung them hard at Wily and Sammy. Wily leapt across to Herbert and took hold of him angrily.

"Come on, Flip!" whispered Binkle. "Now's the time for us to go!"

The two bad bunnies slipped quickly away from the crowd.

Wily was trying to stop Herbert from throwing potatoes at everyone, when suddenly Herbert caught sight of the notice Binkle had put by his seat. He stared as if he couldn't believe his eyes.

"Oh! oh! oh!" he wailed suddenly. "Six throws a penny! It's all a trick – all a trick! Quick, Wily, catch Flip and Binkle."

But Wily wouldn't till Herbert had explained everything.

Then he began to laugh.

"Oh, Herbert!" he cried, wiping his

eyes. "You'll be the death of me one day! You shouldn't be such a silly! Fancy letting yourself be thrown at like that! You might have guessed Flip and Binkle were up to mischief."

"Go and fetch them and punish them!" raged Herbert. "Go on, Wily! They've got lots of pennies, all through me."

Well, in the end Wily did fetch them. He brought them to Herbert, who glared at them fiercely, and growled.

"Don't, Herbert!" begged Wily. "You remind me of when you sat on that seat growling, whilst I threw six potatoes at you – and they all stuck!"

"Punish Flip and Binkle!" ordered Herbert. "They've no business to make money out of me like that!"

Now Binkle hated being punished. An idea came to him.

"I'll give you half the pennies, Herbert," he said, "if you'll let us off being punished. We've got a whole bagful."

Herbert's little eyes shone.

"All right," he agreed at last. "Give me half – but mind, you've been let off very easily!"

As Flip and Binkle went off to the roundabouts, Binkle chuckled. "We *were* let off easily," he said. "We didn't deserve to be, either!"

And they certainly didn't – did they?

The owl, the frog and the
hedgehog

"Hoo-*hoo-hoo!*" cried the owl, one dark night, and flew over the fields on his quiet wings. All the small animals below heard his voice and were terrified.

A small mouse crouched low in the grass. A young rabbit ran to hide in a bush. A toad froze flat to the ground and lay there, looking like a dark clod of earth.

A frog was so scared that he leapt high in the air, and the owl's sharp eyes saw him in the darkness. A frog was a tasty meal. He would like a frog for a change!

He flew lower on his silent wings, looking for the frog. But the little creature was well hidden in a clump of buttercups at the edge of the field.

He felt frightened of the owl – and soon he felt frightened of something else too! A storm was coming, and suddenly lightning flickered and lit up the whole countryside – it lit up the frog's clump of buttercups too. Would that fierce owl see him there?

Then the thunder came, crashing overhead so loudly that the frog was too frightened even to leap away. The mouse nearby fled down a hole. So did the young rabbit. The toad stayed where he was, quite flat on the ground.

The owl did not like storms. Nor did he like the pouring rain that suddenly streamed down. He remembered a hole at the bottom of an old tree.

"I will hide there," he thought. "It would be better to be in a hole than sitting on a branch, because the wind is so strong. What a storm!"

So the owl flew down to the old tree and walked into a little hole right at the very bottom. There he crouched, his head hunched into his feathery shoulders, and waited for the storm to blow over.

The wind blew. It grew to a gale, and soon the old tree was swaying from side to side in the great wind. *Crack!* A bough broke off and fell to the ground. It came to rest just by the hole where the owl was hiding, and it made him jump. Whatever could that noise be? The owl felt worried.

After a while the storm passed over. There was no more lightning, and the thunder rumbled far away in the distance, like a dog growling at an enemy. The pattering of the rain grew lighter, and soon it stopped. A star slid out from behind a cloud.

The owl tried to walk out of the hole at the bottom of the tree. But he couldn't! The little broken bough had wedged itself lightly against the hole.

The owl tried to move it with his beak, and then with one of his feet. But no – it could not be moved from the inside of the hole, only from the outside. The owl was caught!

"*Hoo-hoo-hoo!*" cried the owl angrily, and the frog nearby trembled in the clump of buttercups, because the hooting sounded so near. He did not dare to leap away and show himself. He gave a frightened little croak.

The owl heard him. "Frog, frog, come and help me!" he called.

"No," said the frog. "I do not like owls."

"I'm a kind owl," said the trapped bird. "I would not hurt a dear little frog like you. Come here, frog, I am in a hole in this tree, but a little bough has fallen in front of it. Come here and move it for me."

"No," said the frog. "You have a sharp beak and sharp claws. I am afraid of them."

"Now, now," said the owl, making his

voice as soft as he could. "Do you know that you should always help those in trouble? I would not dream of hurting such a kind little frog as you. See, come over here and tell me if you can push this bough away."

The frog leapt up cautiously. The moon was now out from behind the clouds and he saw clearly that the bough could easily be moved from the outside.

"Well, I will set you free if you promise not to catch me," said the little frog.

"I promise," said the owl, and the frog at once set to work to pull at the bough with his tiny front fingers. Soon the piece of wood slid away from the hole and the owl walked out.

He pounced at once on the frog, who was so surprised and shocked that he couldn't even move.

"You promised you wouldn't catch me if I set you free!" croaked the poor frog.

"Fancy *believing* me!" said the owl. "How very stupid you must be!"

The frog began to croak in terror. "Help! Help me, anyone who is passing! Oh, help!"

There was no one nearby except a prickly hedgehog, looking for his favourite toadstool to nibble. He heard the croaking and ran up to see what was the matter.

The frog told him in his scared, croaking voice, and the hedgehog listened solemnly.

"I am rather a stupid creature," said the hedgehog at last. "Before I do anything I must be sure that I understand your tale properly, so that I may judge who is right. Now, you, frog, were caught in that hole . . ."

"No, no!" said the owl, impatiently. "*I* was in the hole, hedgehog."

"Oh yes – *you* were in the hole," said the hedgehog, "and I came by and heard you calling, and . . ."

"No, you didn't! It was the *frog* who heard me calling!" said the owl. "How stupid you are, hedgehog!"

"Yes – yes, I am stupid," said the hedgehog. "But be patient with me, please. Now, I was in the hole, and you were in the frog, and . . ."

"How could I be in the frog?" hooted the owl, losing his temper. "Haven't you any sense at all?"

"A little. Just a little," said the hedgehog. "I am trying to understand. Now, let me see. The frog was inside you, and the hole came leaping by . . ."

The frog gave a frightened giggle, but the owl glared fiercely and opened his sharp, curved beak as if he would like to peck the hedgehog in rage.

"Poor, stupid creature!" he hooted scornfully. "If you cannot understand words, perhaps you will understand if I *show* you all that happened."

"Well, show me," said the hedgehog. "But do not be so angry, owl, I am only a little hedgehog with a tiny little brain."

The owl stalked back into the hole, hooting angrily. "Now, listen," he said. "I was hiding here, and suddenly something fell outside my hole, and blocked it . . ."

"Like this?" said the hedgehog, and pushed his prickly body quickly against the opening of the hole. He lay there, all his prickles raised, and then he called sharply to the frog, who was still crouched in fear nearby.

"Leap away, frog! You are free! The owl will not come looking for you for quite a long time – he will not be able to leave this hole. I shall not move from here!"

The frog gave a grateful croak and leapt away in a hurry. He disappeared into a ditch.

The owl could hardly believe his ears.

"Get away from this hole!" he hooted in a rage. "How *dare* you block it up! That frog will escape. Let me out."

"No. I am sleepy," said the hedgehog. "I think I will spend the night here, owl, close against your hole. It's no use tearing at me with your claws or your beak. My prickles will protect me.

Now don't hoot so loudly, I want to go to sleep."

And there he lay until daylight, and the owl heard his little grunting snores.

"Well – what a stupid hedgehog, to be sure!" thought the owl, angrily.

But was he stupid? *I* don't think so, do you?

The fairy and the tooth

Anne was feeling rather excited. One of her first teeth had come out that morning, and Mummy had said something rather surprising.

"We'll put it under your pillow tonight, Anne," she said.

"Why?" asked Anne.

"Because the fairies like the little first teeth of children," said Mummy. "Maybe one will come tonight and take your tooth – and perhaps leave you two bright pennies for it!"

That seemed very surprising to Anne. She thought about it all day long – and she made up her mind that she would keep awake that night so that she might see the fairy, if one came!

Well, that night Anne put the tiny white tooth under her pillow, and then she waited and waited for the fairy to come. But no fairy came.

"I shall soon be asleep!" thought Anne, yawning. "I wish I could think of some idea that would wake me up as soon as the fairy took the tooth!"

She did think of an idea! She got out of bed and went to her mother's workbox. She took out a reel of white cotton and broke off a piece of thread. She tied it carefully around the little tooth and put it back under her pillow – and she tied the other end of the cotton to her own little finger!

"Now!" thought Anne, "if the fairy comes and takes the tooth, the thread will pull at my finger, and I shall wake up!"

She fell asleep. She dreamed of all kinds of things, and then suddenly she felt something tugging at her little finger! She woke up at once, and remembered the tooth under the pillow.

The fairy must be there, taking it.

The moonlight streamed into the room, and Anne could see everything quite clearly. By her bed stood a tiny creature, hardly bigger than Anne's biggest doll! She had a mop of bright shiny hair, little pointed ears that stuck up through it, and a pair of silvery wings that grew out from the back of her. There wasn't any doubt at all that it was a fairy.

Anne put out her hand and caught hold of her! She could hold her as easily as a doll. The fairy gave a squeal of surprise and began to wriggle hard. But Anne wouldn't let her go. She lifted her up on to the bed and took a good look at her.

"What a dear little thing you are!" she said. "I did so want to see you. Have you come for my tooth?"

"Yes," said the fairy. "But it was on a bit of cotton. Why did you tie it to your finger?"

"Because I wanted to wake up when

168

you came, and have a look at you,"
said Anne. "Why do you want my little
tooth?"

"Well, it's made of ivory," said the

fairy. "And ivory is nice to carve. I take children's little teeth to Mister Snoodle, and he carves them into tiny toys."

"Oh, how lovely!" said Anne. "What *tiny* toys they must be! I would so like to see them."

"You can't," said the fairy. "Mister Snoodle never lets any but fairy children have them."

"Well, after all, it's *my* tooth!" Anne said. "I don't think I shall let you go until you promise to bring me back the toy that my little tooth is carved into."

"Oh, do let me go," begged the tiny creature in alarm. "I have to be back home before dawn. Everyone will be worried if I don't get back then."

"Well, will you promise to bring me the toy that my tooth makes?" asked Anne. "You needn't leave me the money. I don't want that. I'd rather have my tooth back again, and see what Mister Snoodle has made of it!"

"I can't promise that," said the fairy, beginning to wriggle again. "Don't be unkind, little girl. Let me go. Mister Snoodle badly needs a few teeth just now. He hasn't had any for a long time."

"Well, listen," said Anne. "I have two more teeth that are loose. I promise you that you shall have them for Mister Snoodle when they come out. I'll put them under my pillow. *Now* will you say that I can have this tooth when it's made into a toy?"

"Oh, well, if you really do promise to let me have two more teeth soon, I'll see what I can do about it," said the fairy. "Now please, let me go!"

Anne let her go. The tiny thing spread her wings and fluttered down from the bed. She carried the little tooth with her on its thread. She flew out of the top of the window into the moonlight, and was gone.

Anne felt very excited the next morning. She told her mother all about the fairy.

Mummy laughed. "You dreamed it, darling," she said.

"Well, Mummy, there's no money under my pillow this morning," said Anne, "so I'm sure I *did* catch the fairy and give her my tooth! Oh, won't it be fun if she comes back again with a tiny toy!"

Anne looked under her pillow every morning to see if a little ivory toy was there, but it wasn't.

Then one evening another of her front teeth came out. "I'll put it under my pillow, and maybe the fairy will come back again," thought Anne. "I'll tie it to my finger by a thread again. Then I shall wake."

But, you know, she didn't wake! The fairy came; but this time she had a small pair of scissors with her, and she snipped the thread, so that she could take the tooth without waking Anne! When the little girl found that her tooth was gone, and that she still had a piece of cotton tied round her finger she guessed what had happened.

She hunted carefully under the pillow

and in the bed, and she found the tiniest little toy imaginable. You would love it. It was a very, very small engine, carved out of her old tooth – so small that it could hardly be seen! It had a tiny funnel, and it even had two very, very tiny lamps in front, carved out of the ivory.

"Oh, it's simply beautiful!" cried Anne. "Oh, I'll be afraid of losing it! Mummy, look! What shall I do with this little fairy toy? I mustn't lose it. It's the most precious thing I have!"

"We will put it on your bracelet," said mother. "You shall wear it as a lucky charm. I'll do it for you now. What a lovely little thing it is!"

So Anne wears her engine-tooth on her bracelet, and how all the children love to see it. Isn't she lucky?

She says I am to tell you that it really is a good idea to tie a bit of cotton to a tooth under the pillow – just in *case* you catch a fairy that way, as she did. It's worth trying, isn't it?

The castle without a door

Once upon a time a wizard came to live just outside Brownie Town. He was called Kookle, and no one knew much about him.

"He's building himself a castle on the hill," they said to one another. "He just sits on a stone and says strange words, and the castle grows out of the ground. It is wonderful to watch."

"But it's a very strange castle," said Tinker, a fat jolly brownie. "Do you know that it hasn't any doors at all? How are people going to get in and out? That's what I'd like to know. The windows are far too high up to climb through."

"That's very funny," said the

brownies, and they shook their heads. "Perhaps Kookle is up to mischief of some sort."

It wasn't long before Kookle was very much disliked. He never spoke to the brownies at all, not even when they wished him good day. He turned one of them into a pillarbox one day because the little brownie had accidentally run into him round a corner, and it took Brownie Town a whole week before they could find the right magic to turn the pillarbox back into a brownie.

"He is a horrid wizard," said the little folk. "If only we could get rid of him! But what can you do with someone who lives in a castle without any doors? You can't even get in!"

"He'll do worse mischief yet, you mark my words!" said Tinker.

Now two weeks after that, little Princess Peronel came to stay in Brownie Town with her old nurse, Mother Browneyes. They went walking in Wishing Wood every day.

Then one day a dreadful thing happened. Mother Browneyes came running back from Wishing Wood in a terrible state, crying and groaning in distress.

"What's the matter, what's the matter?" cried the brownies.

"Oh, oh!" wept Mother Browneyes. "I was walking in the wood this morning, when who should come up but Kookle the wizard. And no sooner did he set eyes on pretty little Princess Peronel than he said: 'Ha! I will have her marry me!' And oh, brownies, whatever shall we do? He caught her up then and there and carried her off to his castle!"

"Goodness gracious! What a terrible thing!" cried all the brownies in horror. "Our little Princess with that horrid old wizard! Whatever can we do?"

Well, they decided to go at once to the castle and demand Peronel back. So they trooped off, scores of them, all feeling very angry, but frightened too in case Kookle should turn them into beetles or frogs.

They arrived at the castle, and then of course they remembered that it had no doors. They couldn't knock because there was no knocker, and they couldn't ring because there was no bell. They just stood there wondering what in the world they could do.

"Hie! Hie!" suddenly shouted Tinker, the fat little brownie. "Kookle! Kookle! If you're anywhere in the castle, just listen. Give us back Peronel at once!"

Suddenly the wizard appeared at a window and looked down at the brownies. He laughed loudly.

"Ho!" he cried. "If you want Peronel, come in and get her. Ho, ho, ho!"

"We can't!" yelled Tinker in a rage. "There are no doors!"

"Then go away!" said the wizard. "If you're not all gone by the time I count ten, I'll turn you into muffins! Ha, ha! Now – one, two, three . . ."

But by the time Kookle came to ten, there wasn't a single brownie to be seen.

They had all fled down the hill.

"We *must* do something," said Tinker. "We can't let Peronel be captured like this. But unless we find the door of the castle we can do nothing."

"But there *is* no door," said another brownie.

"There must be one that we can't see," said Tinker. "The wizard comes in and out, doesn't he? But by some kind of magic he has hidden it from our eyes. We must find out where it is. Then even if we can't see it we shall know where to find it and can turn the handle by feeling about for it."

"Well, couldn't we go to the castle tonight and feel all round the walls for the door?" said the other brownies.

So that night six brownies went creeping up to the castle. But alas for them! The wizard heard them, and turned them into kittens, so that Brownie Town was in despair to see six little kittens come running back that night instead of six brownies.

Tinker sat in his cottage and thought very hard. He did so want to rescue Peronel, for he thought she was the prettiest little Princess in all Fairyland. But he could think of no plan.

Next morning when Brownie Town awoke and drew its curtains back, it saw that snow had fallen in the night and all the countryside was white.

"Hurrah!" cried the youngsters. "Now we can build snowmen and play with snowballs."

Then Tinker suddenly had a wonderful idea. He tore out of his cottage to tell the others.

"We will build a big snowman in the field just outside the castle," he said. "The wizard will take no notice of that. But, before the moon is out, I will dress myself in a white cloak, and put on the snowman's hat. You will quickly knock down the snowman and I will take his place! Then I will stand there all night to see where the door is when the wizard comes out for his nightly walk!"

"Oh, Tinker, how clever you are!" cried the others. "That is a wonderful plan!"

"Six of you go and make the snowman now," said Tinker. "Make him about my size. Laugh and talk all the time, as if you were really playing and had forgotten all about Peronel."

So six of the brownies went to the hill on which Kookle's castle stood. The wizard peeped out of a window, but when he saw them building a snowman he took no further notice.

Before nightfall the brownies had built a nice fat snowman just about Tinker's size. They put a row of stones down his front for buttons, and tied a muffler round his neck. They put a hat with a feather on his head, and stuck a pipe in his mouth.

Then off they went down the hill to Brownie Town. Tinker had been very busy meantime making himself a long white cloak. Mother Browneyes had helped him, and together they had sewn six big black buttons down the front. Now the cloak was ready.

So, in the darkness before the moon rose, the seven brownies went silently back up the hill. They quickly knocked the snowman down, and Tinker stood in its place with his long white cloak round him.

The brownies wound the snowman's muffler round his neck, put the snowman's feathered hat on his head and stuck the pipe in his mouth. He was ready!

"Ooh!" said the brownies. "You *do* look like a snowman, Tinker! Well, good luck to you! The moon is just coming up and we must go."

They ran off down the snowy hill, and Tinker was left alone just outside the castle. He felt rather lonely and a bit frightened. Suppose the wizard guessed he wasn't a real snowman? Ooh, that would be dreadful!

The moon came up and soon Tinker could see every brick of the castle quite clearly. He stood on the hillside, hat on head, and pipe in mouth, as still as could be, his white cloak reaching down to his heels. He waited for an hour. He waited for two hours. He waited for three, and four and five. At midnight he was so cold that he was shivering.

"Oh my, I do hope the wizard won't see me shivering," thought Tinker in a fright. "But I can't stop shaking with the cold!"

Just at that moment the clock down in Brownie Town struck twelve. Tinker heard it – and at the same time he heard a voice inside the castle chanting a long string of magic words. Then he saw the door of the castle appearing! He saw it quite clearly, outlined in green flame, with a knocker and a handle, and a very big letter-box.

As Tinker watched, eyes wide open in surprise, he saw the door swing open. The wizard appeared in the opening, and Tinker hurriedly counted the number of bricks from the side of the castle to the door. His heart was thumping so loudly he was afraid the wizard would hear it.

Kookle stepped outside, and at the same moment the door disappeared, the place where it had been becoming part of the wall again. Then suddenly Kookle looked towards Tinker!

"Ha, a snowman!" said the wizard. "Stupid little brownies! How they do waste their time! I've a good mind to knock it all down!"

Tinker nearly died of fright. The wizard came right up to him and snatched the pipe out of his mouth. What Kookle meant to do next Tinker didn't know – but just at that moment a witch came sailing through the air on her broomstick.

"Hey, Kookle! It's time to join the big meeting. Come along!" she called.

In a trice the wizard leapt on to the broom with the witch and sailed off into the moonlit sky. Tinker sighed with relief, for he had been very frightened.

As soon as the wizard was out of sight he threw off his cloak and ran to the castle. He counted fifty-three bricks from the side, then felt for the door.

Almost at once he found the handle and the knocker. He turned the handle and the door swung open. He stepped into the castle and shut the door.

"Peronel! Peronel!" he cried. "Where are you?"

"Here! Here!" cried a tiny voice, far away. "Oh, who are you? Have you come to save me? I am right at the top of the castle!"

Tinker ran to the winding staircase and raced up it, two steps at a time. He was soon breathless for there were many hundreds of stairs. But up he went, and up and up, hoping with all his heart that Kookle would not return until he had rescued the Princess.

At the top of the castle was a small tower where Peronel was imprisoned. Her door was locked and bolted, but Tinker quickly drew the big bolts back, and turned the key, which the wizard had left in the lock.

The little Princess, very pale and thin, for the wizard had given her only bread and water since she refused to marry him, ran to Tinker and flung her arms round his neck.

"Oh, you dear, brave brownie!" she cried. "Thank you so much for saving me!"

"You're not saved yet!" said Tinker. "Quick, we must get out of the castle before the wizard comes back."

Down the hundreds of stairs they ran to the big door, which was easily seen from the inside of the castle. But Tinker couldn't open the door! No matter how he twisted the handle and pulled, that door wouldn't open!

For two hours he tried, but at last he gave up. Only the right magic words could open it from the inside, he realized.

"I know what we'll do!" said Tinker at last. "It isn't a very good plan, but it might work. I expect the wizard will see that the snowman is gone and guess that I am here. He will come rushing into the castle in a fearful rage. Now I've got some string here. I'll tie it from this stool to that chair over there, and when the wizard comes in it will trip him up, and perhaps we shall just have time to run out of the castle."

"Yes, that's a good plan," said Peronel. "But don't let's try to run all the way down the hill to Brownie Town, because the wizard would surely catch us. Just outside is a rabbit-hole. Sandy, a very nice bunny, lives there, and I know he would let us shelter in his burrow till the danger is past."

"That's splendid," said Tinker. He quickly tied the string across the hall just beyond the doorway. Then he and Peronel crouched down in a dark corner near the door.

Suddenly they heard the sound of an angry voice outside. It was the wizard, who had discovered the snowman's cloak on the ground.

"What's this! What's this!" he cried in a fury. "This is a trick! That snowman was a brownie, and he saw me come from the castle! Well, he can't get out. I'll catch him, yes, I will!"

The door flew open and the wizard rushed in. He caught his foot on the string and down he fell with a crash! The door began to close, but Peronel and Tinker slipped through in a flash. The Princess led the brownie to a rabbit-hole, and the two crept down it. The bunny came to meet them, and they explained to him in a whisper.

"Come this way," said Sandy. He led them to a little round room, where there was a tiny fire and a jugful of cocoa warming by it. "Help yourselves to the cocoa, and there are biscuits in that tin. I'm just going to the hillside to see what is happening. Don't be afraid. You are quite safe here."

So Tinker poured Peronel a steaming hot cup of cocoa, and gave her some sugar-biscuits. Then he helped himself, for he was hungry and cold. They sat there, warm and happy, till Sandy the rabbit came back.

"Ha!" said Sandy in glee. "That old wizard is in a dreadful temper. He bumped his head when he fell down, and hurt his knee. He tore down the hillside after you, for of course he didn't know you had come here. He couldn't find you, so he's gone back to his castle to bathe his head. I shouldn't be surprised to find that he leaves Brownie Town quite soon."

All that night the brownie and Peronel stayed with the kind rabbit. Next morning they followed Sandy down many long winding underground passages that led to the bottom of the hill. There they came out into the sunshine and said goodbye to the rabbit.

What a welcome they got in Brownie Town! How all the brownies cheered! And how pleased old Mother Browneyes was to see the Princess again! It really was a very happy morning.

Just as they were all as happy as could be, listening to Tinker's adventures, there came a big BANG! Everyone rushed out to see what was happening, and a very strange sight they saw!

Kookle the Wizard, having made up his mind to leave Brownie Town, had worked a spell on his castle. With a big BANG it had risen into the air and was now sailing away to the east, flapping two huge wings that had grown out of the walls.

"Ooh!" said all the brownies in surprise and joy. "That's the end of the old wizard! He'll never come here again! Let's give a party this afternoon to show we're happy!"

So they did, and the Princess sat next to Tinker, who was happier than he had ever been in his life before. And when Peronel presented him with a lovely gold watch for saving her, you should have heard all the brownies cheer!